COMPUTER CONTROL
AND HUMAN ERROR

COMPUTER CONTROL
AND HUMAN ERROR

Trevor Kletz
with Paul Chung, Eamon Broomfield
and Chaim Shen-Orr

INSTITUTION OF CHEMICAL ENGINEERS

Published by
Institution of Chemical Engineers,
Davis Building,
165–189 Railway Terrace,
Rugby, Warwickshire CV21 3HQ, UK.
IChemE is a Registered Charity

© 1995 Trevor Kletz, Paul Chung,
Eamon Broomfield and Chaim Shen-Orr

ISBN 0 85295 362 3

Printed in the United Kingdom by Galliard (Printers) Ltd, Great Yarmouth.

PREFACE

I am grateful to Paul Chung and Eamon Broomfield for providing a chapter on the use of hazard and operability studies (Hazops) for preventing or reducing errors in computer-controlled plant, and to Chaim Shen-Orr for describing some incidents on a wider range of equipment and — in more detail than I can — the ways in which such errors occur. I am also grateful to the companies where the incidents occurred for allowing me to describe the errors they made. Unfortunately, for reasons I have discussed in my book, *Lessons from Disaster — How Organisations Have No Memory and Accidents Recur* (Institution of Chemical Engineers, Rugby, UK, 1993, Chapter 5), companies are not as willing as they should be, or even as they used to be, to publicize their errors so that others can learn from them. Fortunately, there are still many who realize that if they have fallen into a hole in the road they have a duty to warn other people before they too fall into it. These companies also know that it is in our interest to do so, as those we warn may, in turn, tell us about other hazards.

After one of the incidents described in Chapter 1, Section 1, the company admitted that it had experienced nearly 200 upsets due to hardware and software errors in the previous two years. By failing to publicize them it had deprived itself, and others, of what one of my former ICI colleagues calls 'learning opportunities'.

NOTE FOR AMERICAN READERS
We use the word 'trip' to describe equipment which closes a valve, shuts down a plant or takes similar action when a signal reaches a pre-set value. In the United States such equipment is often called 'an interlock'. We use interlock in a more restricted sense to describe equipment which, for example, prevents one valve being open when another valve is also open (or is shut).

Trevor Kletz

ACKNOWLEDGEMENTS

The research described in Chapter 2 is supported by the Engineering and Physical Sciences Research Council grant J.18217. Paul Chung would also like to thank British Gas and the Royal Academy of Engineering for financial support through a Senior Research Fellowship.

Paul Chung and Eamon Broomfield are grateful to the Association for Computing Machinery for permission to include part of the material previously described in Broomfield and Chung (Reference 10, Chapter 2). Andrew Rushton made helpful comments on a draft of the chapter.

CONTENTS

FORETHOUGHT

*'There is nothing remarkable about it.
All one has to do is hit the right keys at the
right time and the instrument plays itself.'*

Johann Sebastian Bach

INTRODUCTION

All changes and all new technologies introduce hazards as well as benefits[1]. We try to foresee the hazards but do not always succeed, though there are now techniques which help us do so[2,3]. Computers are no exception. In 1982, at the American Institute of Chemical Engineers Loss Prevention Symposium[4], I described some unforeseen incidents that had occurred on computer-controlled process plants and suggested actions which should prevent (or reduce the chance of) similar incidents in the future. None of the incidents I described were major disasters but, I suggested, we should not wait for these to occur but learn now from the experience we had. Nine years later I brought my paper up to date[5] and its publication was followed by requests for further reviews and papers on the same subject[6,7,8,9]. This response made me realize that interest in the subject had grown and that there might be a market for a book bringing together all the incidents that I had described and a few more, plus suggestions for ways of avoiding them in the future. Some of the incidents I describe occurred on systems that are rather simple by modern standards, but they show very clearly the ways in which incidents arise.

The reports on which I have based my accounts in Chapter 1 include some of the most incomprehensible I have ever read. Some computer experts find it hard to write in language that can be understood by operating staff. I have tried to translate their reports into simpler English.

I originally gave my first paper the title 'Hazards of computer control' but I soon realized that the errors were really human failures — failures to foresee or allow for equipment faults or software errors, failures to understand what the system could and could not do, or failures to realize how people respond to displays — and so I changed the title to 'Some human problems with computer control'.

The equipment used is variously described as microprocessors, computers, programmable logic controllers (PLCs) and, particularly in the United Kingdom, as programmable electronic systems (PESs). I have used 'computer' in Chapter 1 and throughout the book as it is the term most widely used, particularly by those who are users of the equipment rather than experts in its design, even though some of the equipment does not contain all the features of a general-purpose digital computer.

Although Chapter 1 describes past events, I try to look forward to the action we should take to avoid further incidents. This is not difficult because familiar incidents are repeating themselves, though in a new context. Computers, as we shall see, provide new opportunities for familiar errors.

In Chapter 2 Paul Chung and Eamon Broomfield survey the attempts that have been made to modify the hazard and operability (Hazop) procedure so that it can be applied to computer-controlled systems. They describe the weaknesses in these modified procedures and show how they can be overcome.

In Chapter 3 Chaim Shen-Orr describes some incidents in a wider range of industries than those discussed in Chapter 1 and shows, by example, how software errors can arise.

Trevor Kletz

REFERENCES IN INTRODUCTION
1. Kletz, T.A., 1982, *Hydrocarbon Processing*, 61 (5): 297.
2. Kletz, T.A., 1976, *Chemical Engineering Progress*, 72 (11): 48.
3. Sanders, R.E., 1993, *Management of Change in Chemical Plants* (Butterworth-Heinemann, Oxford, UK).
4. Kletz, T.A., 1982, *Plant/Operations Progress*, 1 (4): 209.
5. Kletz, T.A., 1991, *Plant/Operations Progress*, 10 (1): 17.
6. Kletz, T.A., 1991, *J Process Control*, 1 (2): 111.
7. Kletz, T.A., 1991, *Control and Instrumentation*, 23 (9): 49.
8. Kletz, T.A., 1993, *Reliability Engineering and System Safety*, 39 (3): 257.
9. Kletz, T.A., 1994, Living with human error on computer controlled plants, in *Foundations of Computer Controlled Process Operations*, edited by Rippin, D.W.T., Hale, C.H. and Davis, J.F. (CACHE, Austin, TX, USA), 95.

1. SOME INCIDENTS THAT HAVE OCCURRED, MAINLY IN COMPUTER-CONTROLLED PROCESS PLANTS

Trevor Kletz

'The real danger came not from automated machines but from automated men.'
Spencer Weart, *Nuclear Fear* (Harvard University Press, 1988)

1. INTRODUCTION

I have classified the incidents I describe as follows, though some of them fall into more than one category:

Equipment faults: the equipment does not perform as expected (Figure 1.1) (page 5)
Most of the failures would have been less serious if the systems as a whole had been designed to minimize the effects of foreseeable hardware failures.

Figure 1.1

Software faults: the program does not perform as expected (page 10)
These can be subdivided into errors in the systems software supplied with the computer, and errors in the applications software written for the particular application. To reduce the chance that there will be errors in the systems software, use only well-tested systems from reputable sources — sometimes difficult in a rapidly changing field. To avoid errors in the applications software considerable effort has to be put into specification and design; in addition, thorough testing is usually recommended. This testing can take longer than design but even

3

then it is usually impossible to cover every possible combination of operating and fault conditions, or even all the operational requirements.

Treating the computer as a 'black box' : something that will do what is wanted without the need to understand what goes on inside it (page 16)
This is probably the most common cause of incidents in the process industries. The number of incidents can be reduced by carrying out hazard and operability studies (Hazops)[1] (see Chapter 2) or applying other systematic hazard identification techniques on the program logic as well as on the process lines. We should ask what the computer will do for all possible deviations (no flow, reverse flow, more flow, more pressure, more temperature, etc), for all operating modes, for all stages of a batch process and for all modes of operation (such as start-up, shutdown and catalyst regeneration) on a continuous process. The applications engineer (systems analyst) should be a member of the Hazop team which should also include at least one other person who understands the program logic. If the team does not include such a person, a dialogue is impossible and the team cannot be sure that the applications engineer understands the process and the design requirements.

Misjudging the way operators respond to the computer (page 26)
This comes close to the last category as a source of error and there is much scope for improving the operator/computer interface. For example, operators may be overloaded by too many alarms or may be confused by displays that look alike.

Errors in the data entered in the computer (page 29)
The computer should not accept data or instructions that are outside specified ranges.

Failure to tell operators of changes in data or programs (page 33)
This has not caused any serious incidents in the process industries, so far as I am aware, but it has caused a serious air accident.

Interference with hardware or software (page 33)
Unauthorized interference with peripheral equipment is more serious than for a traditional plant as, unlike operators, the computer will not know that interference has occurred.

Each of these types of error is now discussed in turn and illustrated by accounts of incidents that have occurred. Some of them illustrate more than one sort of error. Jones[2] lists poor installation and maintenance as another cause of failure.

Although this book describes incidents in computer-controlled plants this does not mean that I am opposed to computer control. Its advantages in greater efficiency and reliability outweigh the disadvantages and, in any case, the disadvantages are not intrinsic or inherent but can be avoided (as with most safety problems), as shown in what follows. The only inherent disadvantage is that the reliability of software cannot be estimated with confidence (see Section 3 of this chapter, page 10).

Ward and Jeffs[3] suggest a different method of classification, based on the stage in the life cycle at which the incident could have been avoided. They list five stages:

(1) Specification — this includes the incidents in my third category and many of those in my other categories.

(2) Design and implementation — this includes most of the incidents in my first two categories, though some of them could have been avoided by better specification.

(3) Installation and commissioning — I have no incidents in this category.

(4) Operation and maintenance — for example, my incidents 5.5 and 8.1 (see pages 28 and 33).

(5) Changes after commissioning, mainly modifications.

An advantage of this method of classification is that it draws attention to the need to examine alternatives critically at the early stages of design — something that we should always do, whatever the method of control.

2.   EQUIPMENT FAULTS

2.1   THE PROBABILITY OF EQUIPMENT FAULTS

We have all been told, when a ticket reservation or bank transaction has gone wrong, that it was a computer error. We all know that this is unlikely and that there was probably an error in the software or input data. Nevertheless hardware faults do occur from time to time.

In the process industries more hardware faults occur in the peripheral equipment — that is, the measuring instruments and transmitters and the control valves — than in the computer itself. The hardware reliability of a computerized control system is therefore similar to that of a conventional hard-wired pneumatic or electrical one[4], and probably a little better.

Bucher and Fretz[5] have described two years' experience with 80 process computers each controlling about 15 loops. They reported that:

• on no occasion did the independent safety installations have to stop the process;

- on no occasion did the watchdogs (see Chapter 3, item 13.1.1 on page 103) have to act;
- ten computer failures occurred as the result of power failures or other external causes;
- thirty input/output modules (which convert digital electric signals into pneumatic pressure or analogue electric signals or vice versa) failed. All the failures were detected by operators before the independent safety systems were activated (but not all operators may be as good).

Wray[6], of the UK Health and Safety Executive (HSE), reports the following failure rates for programmable electronic systems (PESs), HSE's term for computer-controlled systems:

	Failures in 100 years (10^6 hours)
Single system	100
Single system with self-monitoring	50
Dual system	10

In each case the range is a factor of about 3 either way.

Lowe[4] suggests 8 hours as a typical repair time.

The HSE has published a Guidance Note on the use and assessment of PESs[7]. It deals mainly with the hardware and software and devotes little attention to the other sorts of errors discussed in this chapter. It does, however, contain a useful list of points to watch during the design of these systems. It covers all PESs, not just those used for process control.

2.2   SOME EXAMPLES OF EQUIPMENT FAULTS

In my first paper on problems on computer-controlled plant[8] I said that equipment failures were rare, and the figures just quoted suggest that they are not common. Nevertheless since I wrote that paper in 1982 a number of incidents have been drawn to my attention (and, as pointed out in the Preface, many more have occurred). Those reported include the following:

2.2.1   A number of incidents caused by voltage variations[9,10]. The frequency, extent and effects of voltage variations should be considered during design, and hazard studies (such as Hazops and failure mode and effect analyses (FMEAs)) should include a check that this has been done. One cause of voltage variations is lightning, not necessarily in the immediate locality; it can be several miles away. In one case it caused a computer to omit a step in a sequence[9]. The probability of such incidents is low but the consequences could be serious.

Standards for the protection of buildings against lightning are designed to protect the building from damage but may not prevent electronic equipment from being affected by stray currents induced by lightning. In one case a computer controlling a machine was affected by radiation from a welding operation.

A number of similar incidents have occurred in other industries, including fly-by-wire aircraft affected by electronic smog[11].

Several military systems are said to have failed because of electromagnetic interference. During the Falklands War interference from *HMS Sheffield*'s radio prevented the ship's warning system picking up signals from an approaching Exocet missile until too late[12].

Electromagnetic interference and software errors leave no traces behind, no debris or smoking gun. Their role can be inferred only by experiments which try to reproduce the conditions which might have led to the failure. For this reason they may be under-reported[12].

2.2.2   Three raw materials were charged to a reactor through separate lines, each fitted with a valve operated by a computer. The instructions to the computer said that only one valve could be open at a time. Nevertheless indicators showed that at times all three valves were open[9]! They were not fully open but were fluctuating between the open and closed positions. The unexpected behaviour was believed to be due to an oscillation caused by rapid scanning of the three valve position indicators.

Perhaps we should ask, during Hazops, if it is possible for valves to oscillate and, if so, what the results will be.

2.2.3   A plant was fitted with relief valves and with remotely-operated blowdown valves in parallel. All the valves discharged into the same flare system. If a number of the relief valves and the corresponding blowdown valves were open at the same time, the vent system could be overloaded. However, no operator, not even the most inept, would open the blowdown valve on a vessel when the relief valve was already open. Fortunately, the designers realized that a single hardware fault could result in all the blowdown valves opening at the same time and the hardware was modified to prevent this occurring. A restriction in the line from each pair of valves (relief valve and blowdown valve) might have been fitted to limit the total flow but this might have restricted the rate at which equipment could be depressured.

2.2.4   A hardware failure caused a number of electrically-operated isolation and control valves to open at the wrong time. Three tonnes of hot polymer (at 300°C) was discharged onto the floor of a building and nitrogen at a gauge

7

pressure of 27 bar, used for blanketing the vessels from which the spillage occurred, was also released. The failure occurred in a watchdog (see Chapter 3, item 13.1.1, page 103), intended to give warning of failures. The fault affected the input/output (I/O) modules and they produced random settings[9,13,14].

This incident shows the importance of having a fully independent safety system as discussed later (item 3.1, page 10). On the plant concerned, the trip systems were independent of the control computer but the designers did not realize that other safety systems — such as interlocks to prevent valves being open at the wrong time — should also be independent (see note in the Preface on the meaning of the word 'interlock'). In addition, watchdogs should not cause failures elsewhere. A Hazop which questioned what would happen if foreseeable hardware failures occurred, at each stage of a batch, would have disclosed the design faults.

Note that the initial hardware failure was merely a triggering event. It would not have had serious results if the watchdog and the interlocks had been truly independent. The incident could have been prevented by better design.

2.2.5   On another occasion a diagnostic circuit card was inserted in such a way that it prevented the watchdog operating.

2.2.6   Measuring instruments or control valves are connected to control computers through digital input/output modules (DOMs) which often handle eight or more inputs or outputs. If a module fails, many control loops may be put out of action. The damage can be minimized by re-arranging the way in which the modules are used. Thus failure of a DOM in the arrangement shown in Figure 1.2(a) disables three pumps; the arrangement shown in Figure 1.2(b) is better[15].

2.2.7   On 3 June 1980 the screens at US Strategic Air Command showed that missiles were heading towards the US. The immediate cause of the false alarm was a hardware failure. The system was tested by sending alarm messages in which the number of missiles was shown as zero. When the hardware failure occurred the system replaced zero by random numbers. The software had not been designed in such a way as to minimize the effects of hardware failure[16,17].

2.2.8   A valve opened for no apparent reason, causing a line rupture and a discharge of gas to atmosphere. Investigation showed that this was due to a missing ground connection on a data highway terminal. The fault had been present since the start-up of the plant six years earlier but was not revealed until a particular combination of circumstances arose[3]. The fault was a time bomb, like many of the software errors described later.

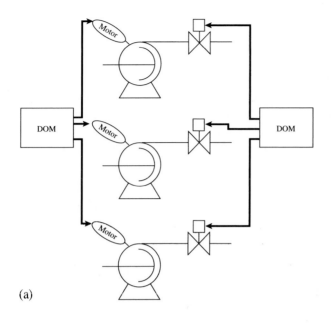

(a)

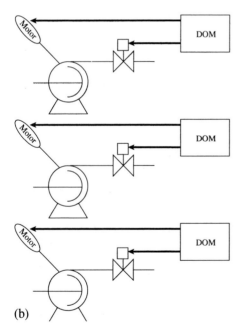

(b)

Figure 1.2   (a) Failure of either DOM (digital output/input module) affects all three pumps. (b) A better arrangement — failure of a DOM affects only one pump. (Reproduced by permission of the American Institute of Chemical Engineers.)

9

Many of the incidents just described could have been prevented by redundancy and thus by better design or specification.

2.3   FAILURES OF PERIPHERAL EQUIPMENT

As already stated, most hardware failures occur in peripheral equipment, not in the computer, and are therefore, strictly speaking, outside the scope of this book. Nevertheless, a couple may be of interest.

One occurred on a microwave oven; the interlock which should have isolated the power supply when the door was opened failed to operate. The manufacturers were told that the door would be opened four times per day and chose the interlock accordingly. It was actually opened 200 times per day and ultimately the contactors became welded together[3]. The incident could have been prevented by better specification.

It is, of course, bad practice to assume that a trip or interlock will always work. The power supply should have been isolated before the door was opened. If we assume that trips or interlocks will always work, and do not check that they have done so, the demand rate on them will be much higher than assumed in their design and the hazard rate will be correspondingly higher[1].

The second incident occurred on a semi-submersible offshore drilling rig which nearly capsized due to the failure of the hydraulic control system. A filter had been left out of the hydraulic lines, so debris accumulated and damaged the seats of the valves, preventing them closing. The possibility of valve failure was not considered when the design of the control system was modified[3].

3.   SOFTWARE FAULTS

3.1   THE NATURE OF SOFTWARE FAULTS

A remark by Wray[18] illustrates the difficulty of locating software errors even when we know they exist. He writes, 'I was involved with a machine which failed to stop when a man put his hand through a photo-electric guard; fortunately he wasn't injured but I've now got a program of 279 pages of assembly code with the comments in German and which I suspect contains a fault'. In the end he scrapped the software and started again.

Hardware errors are usually probabilistic and random — that is, they can occur anywhere at any time (equipment is rarely in use long enough for wear-out failures to occur). In contrast, software errors are systemic — that is, they will always occur when the same conditions arise. As these conditions may arise infrequently, software errors can lie in wait like time bombs. They may not occur, for example, until a particular alarm condition occurs at a particular stage in a batch process.

According to one estimate, errors in the systems software (the software supplied with the computer) can vary between one error in thirty lines at worst and one error in a thousand lines at best[19].

Failures due to faults in the hardware can be prevented by duplication (redundancy) but failures due to faults in the software cannot be prevented by duplicating it. If very high software reliability is required, Wray[18] recommends two independent computer systems, each using a different software program. The two programs should be written in different languages, using independent specifications, by programmers who have never met and have been trained apart. Even then there may be a common mode error in the specification. So far as I am aware, this method has never been used in the process industries, but it has been used for space and aircraft systems (see Chapter 3, item 13.1.2, page 103).

The value of training the two programmers apart is shown by the work of Gondran[20]. Twenty-eight students were given a design problem. As expected there were many errors. If p_1 and p_2 are the probabilities that errors 1 and 2 occur in a design, then the probability p_{12} that both occur in the same design is not $p_1 p_2$ as expected but somewhat greater. In fact p_{12} exceeds 3.3 $p_1 p_2$ with 95% confidence. It seems that similar training led some students to look at problems in similar ways (see Chapter 3, item 13.2.2, page 105).

Apart from any faults present in the original software, modifications can introduce faults. Treat software changes as seriously as changes to plant or process and subject them to similar control (see Introduction and items 3.2.2 and 6.5, pages 14 and 31). Make no change until it has been authorized by a senior and responsible person who first carries out a systematic study of the consequences by Hazop or a similar technique. Access to software should be restricted. In the incident described in item 2.2.4 on page 7, in which liquid polymer was discharged onto the floor, the software had been extensively modified and was very different from that originally installed. A detailed study of the software, after the incident, identified a hundred defects. As there were eight similar units on the plant, 800 changes had to be made. These needed ten man-years' work[14].

As already stated, software errors can be reduced by thorough testing but the number of possible combinations of operating and fault conditions is usually so large that it is impracticable to test every possibility (see Chapter 3, Section 6, page 88 and item 13.4, page 107). Leveson[21] therefore recommends that instead of relying on attempts to make the software ultra-reliable, we should try to make the plant safe even if the software is unreliable. This can be done in two ways:
• by installing independent trips and interlocks, the defence-in-depth approach (if we use this method the trips should be truly independent, as discussed both

above and below); or, preferably,

• by developing, when possible, user-friendly and inherently safer designs — that is, plant and equipment designs in which the hazards are avoided rather than kept under control. For example, it is often possible to make the inventory of hazardous material so low that it hardly matters if it all leaks or explodes; on other occasions a safer material can be used instead[22].

Of course, we should design such plants whenever we can, regardless of the type of control, and be on our guard against the view, sometimes heard but more often implicit, 'Don't worry about the hazards; the control system will keep them under control'. This is not a view held by control engineers, who know only too well the limitations of their equipment and the ways in which it can be neglected, but it is sometimes held by other engineers.

User-friendly plants have been defined as those in which human error or equipment failure will not seriously affect safety, output or efficiency[22]. Human errors include software errors and other errors made during the design and operation of a computer system.

If any calculations are carried out as part of a control program, their accuracy should be checked by independent calculation. For example, manual checks of a program for calculating pipe stresses showed that gravitational stresses had been left out in error[23].

Gondran[20] quotes the following figures for the probability that there will be a significant error in the applications software of a typical microprocessor-based control system:

Normal systems: 10^{-2} to 10^{-3}.
To achieve 10^{-4} considerable extra effort is needed.
To achieve 10^{-6} this additional effort has to be as great as the initial development effort.

Andow[24] considers that the figure for normal systems is too optimistic for all but the simplest systems.

While figures such as these may apply on average, there is no way of proving that a particular program (except a very simple one) is free from errors or that the probability that they are present is below any specified level. For this reason the ultimate safety protection should always be independent of the control system and, in addition, many organizations insist that it be hard-wired. In the UK the Health and Safety Executive normally holds this view. Some organizations will accept an independent computer system, and in some cases the ultimate safety system may require calculations which it would be difficult or impossible to carry out without a microprocessor — for example, estimates of trends such as rate of temperature rise.

We need to know the demand rate on the ultimate safety system — that is, how often it will be called upon to operate — before we can design it. The demand rate depends on the reliability of the control system and so we have to make an estimate of it, uncertain though it may be. (The demand rate also depends on the probability that operators will intervene in time to prevent a trip; see item 2.3 on page 10.)

Alarms can be part of the control system, but not trips and emergency shutdown systems. Those interlocks which prevent one valve being opened unless another is shut are in an intermediate category. They are often part of the control system but where the consequences of failure are serious (as in the case described in item 2.2.4 on page 7, in which they should have prevented drain valves opening), they should be independent.

Another example: many runaway reactions have occurred in batch reactors because the stirrer (or circulation pump) stopped but addition of reactants continued. The added material forms a separate layer and when the stirrer (or pump) is restarted, there is an uncontrolled reaction. It is therefore normal practice to provide an interlock to stop addition of reactants if mixing is lost. On one plant the computer control system, for an unknown reason, did not start the stirrer until much of the raw material had been added. This led to an uncontrolled reaction and a release of toxic gas. The interlock should have been independent of the computer[14].

In the UK's Sizewell B atomic power station, as well as a high-integrity computer-based control system, there are two protective systems, both independent of the control system and both based on two-out-of-four voting. The primary system is microprocessor-based; if it fails to act there is a secondary system based on conventional analogue trip units and magnetic logic elements. The reliability of the primary system could not be quantified but the designers had to demonstrate that the design and testing produced software of a quality commensurate with the reliability required.

Complete testing was impossible but the tests covered a variety of operating conditions and the majority of the protective system's functions. Altogether over 60,000 tests were carried out. A few minor anomalies were revealed[25,26].

3.2   SOME INCIDENTS CAUSED BY SOFTWARE ERRORS

3.2.1   Leveson and Turner[27] have described a software failure which may have lessons for the process industries even though it occurred in the medical industry. The Therac–25, a development of earlier machines for producing high voltage electron beams for irradiating cancer patients, was introduced about

1984. Between 1985 and 1987 eleven cancer patients, in different hospitals in the USA and Canada, received massive overdoses of radiation, up to a hundred times more than their doctors had prescribed. The manufacturers of the machine at first said that this was impossible as the control software was 100,000 times more reliable than that on the earlier Therac–20 model which had never had this problem. They were unable to reproduce the fault. A persistent hospital physicist discovered the cause: an overdose occurred when the prescription data was edited very quickly, so quickly that a key was pressed before the computer had finished editing the previous input; this could be done only by an operator who had repeated the procedure many times. In contrast, when the manufacturer's experts arrived to test the equipment they naturally did so slowly and deliberately and failed to repeat the fault. Leveson and Turner describe the software error in detail.

On this equipment it was not sufficient to press the right keys in the right order — see the quotation from J.S. Bach at the front of the book. The timing was also important.

On earlier Therac models a hard-wired interlock prevented an overdose. If an operator edited the data too quickly the machine simply tripped out. The operator then tried again, perhaps a little more slowly and deliberately than usual, to make sure that the right keys were pressed. The inconvenience was trivial and no-one reported a fault. (If my microwave oven, which has eleven keys in addition to the numbered ones, fails to come on I assume I have programmed it wrongly so I press the cancel button and try again.) On the Therac–25 the software was improved and a safety analysis showed that the probability of the computer selecting the wrong energy level was 10^{-11} (presumably per demand) so the hard-wired trip was left off.

One wonders how scientifically trained people can accept such garbage. Software errors apart, an electrical or mechanical phenomenon so rare that it has never yet been observed could have a probability of occurrence far greater than 10^{-11} per demand.

The Therac incident is discussed further in Chapter 3, item 13.4, page 107.

3.2.2   A control program was modified to increase the number of functions carried out. The supplier agreed that some displays could be moved from memory to disk in order to make more memory available. On restart the computer crashed three times within 12 days. Each time control of the plant was lost for four minutes and batches were ruined. Each crash was due to overload and the original system was restored[28].

3.2.3   According to press reports[29], a mysterious software fault has occurred on Boeing 747s. On 32 occasions (once in every million flight-hours) planes operating on autopilot have started to roll over without warning. All but one of the incidents occurred during daylight when the error was easily noticed. The other incident occurred at night and the plane fell 10,000 feet before it was righted. The autopilot manufacturer has been unable to find the fault. The new Boeing 747–400 uses a different autopilot system.

3.2.4   Another incident occurred on a plant in which ethylene oxide is manufactured by reacting ethylene gas with pure oxygen. The mixture was circulated through a loop reactor, with continuous removal of product and addition of fresh raw materials. The oxygen concentration was close to the explosive limit and so a high-integrity protective system was needed to prevent an explosion. If reaction conditions — particularly the oxygen concentration — moved outside the control limits, the plant was tripped: three valves in the oxygen inlet line closed and two bleed valves between them opened. The set of five valves was duplicated so that the system could be tested with the plant on-line, without interrupting or upsetting production (see Figure 1.3).

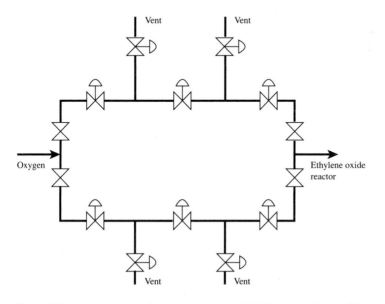

Figure 1.3   Arrangement of valves on oxygen inlet line to ethylene oxide reactor.

Testing was carried out automatically by a mobile computer. The plant was put on stand-by with both sets of oxygen valves closed. The computer was plugged in and connected to oxygen line A. When the test on this line was complete the tester switched the computer to oxygen line B. As a result of a software error the computer responded by momentarily opening one set of oxygen isolation valves. Some oxygen entered the mixture already present in the reactor, the oxygen concentration rose into the flammable range and an explosion blew out a gasket on the ethylene line. The escaping gas ignited and the flame impinged on the 48 inch (1.2 m) reactor loop line. A flange failed and 3 tonnes of gas escaped, engulfing the structure in fire. No-one was injured but damage to instruments and cables was extensive and the plant was off-line for several months. The error was not a slip in writing the software but rather an error in its structure.

3.2.5   As the result of a fault in the software a computer opened the vent valve on the wrong vessel. 14 tonnes of carbon dioxide were vented and lost. The fault was due to an error, probably a slip, in writing the coding[14]. The error was apparently not detected during testing.

Software errors are the equivalent of typesetting or grammatical errors in written instructions. However, those who read written instructions usually know what is meant, despite the errors, and act accordingly. They are unlikely to follow literally the notice in a kitchen which said, 'Please rinse teapots and then stand upside down in the sink' (Figure 1.4), but a computer does not know what is meant and cannot act accordingly.

However, eliminating typesetting and grammatical errors does not make a written instruction correct, and in the same way eliminating software errors does not make software correct. Its structure or logic may make it incapable of doing what we want. This is discussed further in the next section.

4.   TREATING THE COMPUTER AS A 'BLACK BOX'

A number of incidents have occurred because a computer failed to perform in the way that the designer or operators expected it to perform. These incidents did not occur because of equipment faults or errors in the software but because of errors in the logic. These errors may have been present because the applications engineer (systems analyst) did not understand the designer's or operators' requirements, or was not given sufficiently detailed instructions covering all eventualities. They may have been caused because the operators did not understand what the computer could and could not do. People will often do what we

16

Figure 1.4   People can usually decode the meaning intended even when the instructions are inaccurate.

want them to do even though we have not covered the point precisely in our instructions. People can decode the meaning intended even though the instructions are vague or even erroneous; we know what is meant if we are told to 'Save soap and waste paper' or told to follow the advice in Figure 1.5 (see page 18). A computer, in contrast, can do only what it is told to do, as shown by the following incidents:

4.1   This incident occurred on a rather simple batch reactor control system (see Figure 1.6 on page 19) but illustrates my point very clearly. Lessons can often be distilled more easily from simple systems than from complex ones. The computer was programmed so that, when a fault occurred, an alarm would sound and all controlled variables would be left as they were until the operator told the program to continue.

    An alarm indicated a low oil level in a gearbox. It occurred at a time when the catalyst had just been added to the reactor and the computer had just started to increase the flow of cooling water to the reflux condenser. As instructed, the computer kept the flow small, the reactor overheated, the relief

17

Figure 1.5(a)   A man can do what we want him to do. A computer can do only what it is told to do ...

Figure 1.5(b) ... but some men behave like computers.

valve lifted and the contents of the reactor were discharged to atmosphere. No-one was injured but there were complaints about the pollution.

The operators responded to the alarm by looking for the cause of the low oil level. By the time they had established that the level was normal and the low level signal was false, the reactor had overheated. A Hazop (see Chapter 2,

18

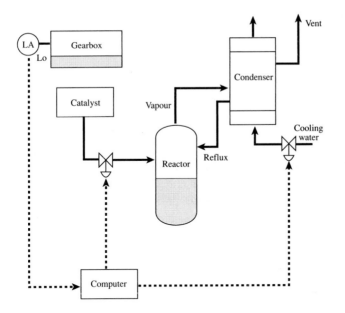

Figure 1.6   Computer-controlled batch reactor.

Section 3) had been carried out on the design but those involved did not understand what went on inside the computer and treated it as a 'black box' — something that will do what we want it to do without the need to understand what goes on inside it. They should have subjected the program logic to a Hazop and asked:

● what action will the computer take for all possible deviations (no flow, more or less flow, more or less pressure, etc, including all alarm conditions) at all stages of the batch?

● what will the consequences be?

● if the consequences are hazardous or prevent efficient operation, what other instructions should be given to the computer and/or what independent backup system should be installed?

The applications engineer should be a member of the Hazop team and, as stated at the beginning of the chapter, the team should include at least one other person able to understand the program logic. If the team does not include such a person, a dialogue is impossible and the team cannot be sure that the applications engineer understands the process requirements.

The program logic may not have been defined when the normal Hazop of the equipment is carried out and the applications engineer may not even have been appointed. In such cases another Hazop should be carried out when the

19

program logic is available (see item 4.7 on page 24). It is better, however, to define the control system and its logic and appoint the applications engineer earlier in the design process.

Engineers like to know how things work and are usually keen to take them to bits. It is therefore surprising that so many of us are willing to take computer-controlled systems on trust. It is not necessary for us to understand the electronics but we do need to understand the logic of the program, to know what it will and will not do in all the circumstances that may arise. Control engineers, like all experts, are usually fully aware of the limitations of their designs; their customers, however, may have a trusting but unrealistic faith in their power.

The incident is a good example of the ill-thought-out results of blanket instructions (to computers or people). Each fault or alarm condition should be considered separately, for all stages on a batch plant and for all operating modes (start-up, shutdown, catalyst regeneration, etc) on a continuous plant.

When the operating manager asked the applications engineer to ensure that all controlled variables are left as they are when an alarm sounds, did he intend that the cooling water flow should be left unchanged or the temperature of the reactor left unchanged? The manager probably never thought about it. A Hazop would have provided an opportunity to discuss this point.

Note also that even the most inept operator, whatever the instructions, would have increased the water flow before going to look at the gearbox. As I have already said, people can do what we want them to do, computers can only do what they are asked to do.

4.2   A computer was controlling a batch reaction on a chemical plant during the night when summer time (daylight saving) ended and the clocks had to be put back one hour. The operator reset the clock in the computer so that it indicated 2 a.m. instead of 3 a.m.. The computer then shut the plant down for an hour until the clock indicated 3 a.m. again[18]. Perhaps Hazop studies should consider reverse flow of time as well as reverse flow of liquids!

This incident is amusing but, before you laugh, what happens on your plants when the clocks are reset?

4.3   A steel plant furnace was started up from cold shutdown after repair. The temperature indicator was out of order and continually registered a low temperature. The computer therefore supplied the maximum fuel gas rate to the furnace and continued to supply it after an hour when the furnace was hot. After four hours the furnace was seriously damaged[21].

Instrument failure is a foreseeable event and should be considered during design, by means of a failure mode and effect analysis (FMEA) or in some other way. One wonders what the operators were doing. Did they have such confidence in the computer that they never bothered to look at the information displays? If the furnace had not been controlled by a computer even the most inept operator would have suspected that something was wrong if the temperature had not changed after an hour. The computer could, of course, have been programmed to sound an alarm if the temperature did not change after a period of time, but no-one recognized the need to tell it to do so. A Hazop or FMEA could have shown the need.

A similar incident occurred on another plant. The computer 'froze' and for two hours the operator did not notice that the display had not changed. As a result a vessel was overfilled. It is easy to show the time on the display screen but this had not been done, and there was no independent high level alarm[14].

These incidents illustrate a point that applies to almost all the incidents described in this chapter: computers do not introduce new errors but they provide new opportunities for making old errors; they allow us to make more errors faster than ever before. Incidents will occur on any plant if we do not check readings from time to time, if we do not look out for instruments which are out of order or stuck, or if our instructions do not allow for foreseeable failures of equipment.

4.4   A pump and various pipelines were used for several different duties — transferring methanol from a tank truck to storage, charging it to the plant and moving recovered methanol back from the plant (see Figure 1.7 on page 22). A computer set the various valves and monitored their positions.

A tank truck was emptied. The pump had been started from the panel but had been stopped by means of a local button. The next job was to transfer some methanol from storage to the plant. The computer set the valves but as the pump had been stopped manually it had to be started manually. When the transfer was complete the computer told the pump to stop but as it had been started manually it did not stop and a spillage occurred[30].

A thorough Hazop would probably have disclosed the fact that this error could have occurred and the control system could have been modified or, better still, separate lines could have been installed for the various different movements, thus greatly reducing the opportunities for error. The incident shows how easily errors in complex systems can be overlooked, if they are not thoroughly analysed. In addition it illustrates the paradox that, as I have shown elsewhere[22], we are very willing to spend money on complexity but are less willing to spend it on simplicity. Yet the simpler solution — independent lines, actually installed after the spillage — makes errors much less likely, and may not be more expensive if lifetime costs are considered. Control systems need

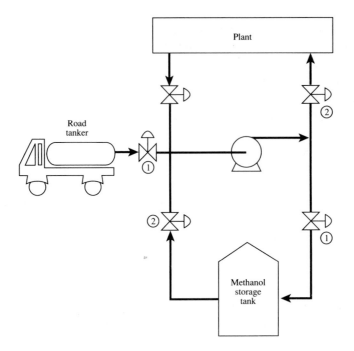

Figure 1.7   A pump and lines, controlled by a computer, were used for several different jobs. The pump could also be started and stopped locally.
① Valves open for first job; others closed.
② Valves open for second job; others closed.

regular testing and maintenance which roughly doubles their lifetime cost (even after discounting) while extra pipelines involve little extra operating cost.

A similar error occurred on another plant. The motor valve in the transfer line between a reactor and a neutralization vessel failed to open when the 'automation system' told it to open. The foreman opened the valve manually. As a result it did not close automatically when the transfer was complete. There was no non-return valve in the transfer line and steam from the neutralization vessel flowed backwards into a pump tank (located between the reactor and the neutralization vessel; see Figure 1.8) and reacted violently with a heel of product that was left there[31]. A Hazop had been carried out on the design but it was not done with any great thoroughness as it was 'just a pumping operation'.

There were, of course, weaknesses in the design as well as the control system. After the explosion the pump tank was removed and the reactor emptied by pressurization with nitrogen.

4.5   Another incident occurred on a pressure filter which was controlled by a computer. It circulated the liquor through the filter for two hours. As more solid was deposited on the filter the pressure drop increased. To measure the pressure drop the computer counted the number of times the pressure of the air in the filter needed to be topped up in 15 minutes. It had been told that if less than five top-ups were needed, filtration was complete and it could move on to the next phase, smoothing the cake. If more than five top-ups were needed, the liquor was circulated for a further two hours.

There was a leak of compressed air into the filter which misled the computer into thinking that filtration was complete. It signalled this fact to the operator who opened the filter door and the entire batch, liquid and solid, was spilt.

To be fair to the computer, or rather to the programmer, the computer had detected that something was wrong — there was no increase in power consumption during smoothing — and had signalled this fact by stopping the operation but the operator ignored this warning sign, or did not appreciate its significance[30].

Again a Hazop would probably have disclosed the weakness in the system for detecting the pressure drop through the cake and changes could have

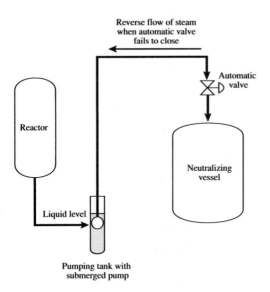

Figure 1.8   The automatic valve was opened manually so it did not close automatically when the transfer from the reactor to the neutralizing vessel was complete. Steam from the neutralizing vessel entered the pumping tank and reacted with a heel of liquid that had been left there.

been made. In particular, it would be desirable to provide some means of preventing the operator opening up the filter while it is full of liquid. Many accidents have occurred because operators opened up autoclaves or other pressure vessels while they were up to pressure[32]. Opening up a vessel while it is full of liquid at low pressure is not as dangerous but nevertheless dangerous enough.

4.6   This incident occurred on a plant where the possibility of a leak of liquid had been foreseen and a sump had been provided into which any leaks would drain. A level alarm would then sound. Unfortunately, when a leak occurred it fell onto a hot surface; most of it evaporated, leaving a solid residue, and none entered the sump. The leak was not detected for several hours.

The operators could have detected that something was wrong by a careful comparison of trends in a number of measurements, but they saw no need to make such a comparison as they were not aware of any problem. The relevant measurements were not normally displayed and had to be called up. Afterwards the operators said that the spillage would have been detected earlier if the chart recorders had been left in the control room when the computer was installed. The computer could have been programmed to carry out mass balances, compare readings for consistency and/or to sound an alarm (or, better, display a message advising the operators that something was amiss) when unexpected measurements were received, but no-one had foreseen the need to ask it to do so[33]. Some companies now install additional screens, without keyboards, so that selected measurements can be displayed continuously. (Though not relevant to this case a computer can detect the absence of noise in measurements that are 'stuck' and can warn the operator if full-scale deflection is reached or approached on a measuring instrument.)

Operators should, of course, be encouraged to 'let their fingers do the walking' and look every so often at the displays under their control; like everyone else they should manage by looking for changes or trends rather than managing by exception — that is, waiting until an alarm or trip shows that something is wrong. We would need much more reliable trips than we have if operators always waited for them to operate (see item 2.1, page 5).

4.7   The experience of one plant shows the value and limitations of Hazop studies in preventing incidents similar to those just described[34]. A Hazop was carried out on one unit during design, but the program logic was not studied as it had not yet been designed. 13 recommendations were made, a rather low number for the size of the unit. A further study was therefore carried out later, when the logic program was available. This study took 12 hours, spread over four meetings, and made 55 recommendations. Most of the logic program had to be rewritten but it has performed flawlessly. As a spin-off the site standard for watchdogs and their wiring was rewritten.

On the same site a computer was installed to replace about 80 conventional PID (proportional, integral, derivative) controllers. The key members of the Hazop team — the applications, process and loss prevention engineers — were inexperienced and too optimistic. (They were not aware of the golden rule: all plants may be operated by Murphy and maintained by his engineering colleagues, Rube Goldberg[35] in the United States, Heath Robinson[36] in the United Kingdom.) As a result the Hazop lasted only two and a half hours and made only seven minor recommendations. Six weeks after start-up the flare system became full of liquid hydrocarbons. At least two alarms were ignored by the operators who said afterwards that there were far too many alarms on the unit. They sounded so often that they were ignored.

The Hazop team had realized that the flare system might fill with liquid and they added a high level alarm. However, they did not ask:

- how many alarms are there?
- should the alarm start up a pump automatically to lower the liquid level?
- does the alarm appear on a display (screen page) that could be confused with another (see next item)?
- what signals will be lost at the same time as the alarm if there is a hardware (for example, a card) failure?

As we gain more experience of the application of Hazop to computer logic, changes to the usual Hazop questions will be seen to be desirable (see Chapter 2).

4.8   It may be useful to summarize the recommendations made in Section 4 which apply to all plants, whether they are controlled by computers or people, but which are particularly important on computer-controlled plants as the computer cannot distinguish between what we say and what we mean (see Figure 1.5 on page 18). They are, of course, additional to the main recommendation of this section that the logic of the computer software — that is, the strategy we expect it to follow and the precise way in which it does so — should be subjected to a hazard and operability study (Hazop).

- Do not issue blanket instructions — that is, instructions which apply to all equipment at all times — unless you are certain that they really do apply regardless of special circumstances such as start-up, shutdown, low rate, stand-by, re-generation, 'running-in' of new catalyst or furnace brickwork and all stages of batch processes (see item 4.1 on page 17).

• Look at all readings from time to time to see if there are any unexpected changes. If the plant is computer-controlled and there is no instrument panel, look through the display pages. (The computer can be programmed to do this for us, but do not rely on it 100%.) Show the time on display pages so the operators can see if the computer has frozen (see items 4.3 and 4.6 on pages 20 and 24).

• Allow for foreseeable failures of equipment (see item 4.6 on page 24 and Section 2 on page 5).

• Look out for instruments which are out of order or stuck. A computer can be programmed to detect the absence of noise, unusual readings or the absence of change (see items 4.3 and 4.6 on pages 20 and 24).

• Look out for inconsistencies in readings. Again, a computer can be programmed to detect them but only those that we have asked it to detect (see item 4.6 on page 24).

• Aim for simplicity. It is often cheaper but even when it is not it may be worth paying a little more for it, as simpler plants contain less equipment which can go wrong and provide fewer opportunities for errors (see item 4.4 on page 21 and Reference 22).

• Do not omit or rush Hazops just because the equipment being studied is 'only a pump and a couple of tanks', an off-plot or a service (see item 4.4 on page 21 and Section 2.8 of Reference 1).

5. MISJUDGING THE WAY OPERATORS RESPOND TO THE COMPUTER

Misjudging the way operators respond comes close to the last category (Section 4) as a source of error and there is much scope for improving the operator/computer interface. In 1973 Edwards and Lees wrote, 'hardly any human factors effort has yet been devoted to human factors software in any area. Here is a rich research field where the problems of designing languages and systems to suit the human users offers a fascinating, though difficult, challenge to ergonomics'[37]. Since then, much work has been done in this area but not as much as the problems require. Too many computer specialists, like too many other engineers, are not interested in human factors problems. Instead of designing 'round holes' (equipment and procedures) to suit the round shape of people, they find it easier to design square holes and hope, despite the evidence to the contrary, that people will change their shape to suit the holes which have been designed.

Here are some incidents that could have been prevented by better design of the operator/computer interface. Others are described in item 4.6 (page 24) and in Chapter 3, Section 10 (page 96).

26

5.1   Item 4.7 (page 24) illustrates the most common error of this type: alarm inflation. Adding alarms to a computer is cheap and easy, the operators like to know when a measurement changes on a page that is not on display at the time so that they can intervene if necessary, so more and more alarms are added. When a serious upset occurs, dozens — even hundreds — of alarms may sound at once. As a result, the operators have no idea what is happening and switch off (themselves, not the computer). Low priority alarms can divert operators' attention from more important ones[38]. This occurred at Three Mile Island where more than 500 annunciators changed status in the first minutes, more than 800 in the first two minutes.

Fitting alarms illustrates the maxim that if we deal with each problem as it arises, the end result may be the opposite of that intended.

If an operator wishes to know when a measurement changes, but the change does not require immediate action by the operator, the computer can be programmed to display a message instead of sounding an alarm.

When a power failure occurred on one plant the computer printed a long list of alarms. The operator did not know what had caused the upset and did nothing. A few minutes later an explosion occurred. Afterwards the designer admitted that the operator had been overloaded with too much information but asked why the operator did not assume the worst and carry out an emergency shutdown of the plant. Unfortunately, when people are overloaded by too much information they tend, as already stated, to 'freeze' and do nothing. They do not say to themselves, 'I don't know what is happening so I'll assume the worst and trip the plant'. Computers make it easy to overload many people with too much information — not just operators.

Another problem with alarms is that the information that operators need for handling them is often distributed amongst several pages of the display[38]. It should be possible to link together on a special page for each significant alarm the information needed for dealing with it.

5.2   The pages of a computer display sometimes look alike. This saves development time, and thus cost, but can cause confusion during an emergency. An operator may turn to the wrong display page and not realize he has done so. For example, on one plant an operator could call up a list of valves, select one of them by entering a two-digit number and then operate it. Inadvertently, the operator called up the list for the wrong section of the plant, did not notice what had happened — as all the lists looked alike with similar numbering — and opened the wrong valve. Many tonnes of chemical were lost to drain[3].

Function keys often have different functions on different display pages. This can lead to errors[39].

Information needed by operators is sometimes displayed alongside information on productivity needed by managers and other technologists. This confuses the operators. The two sorts of data should be displayed on separate pages[40].

5.3   To reduce the chance that operators will enter incorrect data or instructions, computers are sometimes programmed so that after someone has entered information and pressed the 'Enter' button, the data or instructions are displayed for checking. Then 'Enter' is pressed a second time. After a while new operators are told to enter information and then press 'Enter' twice. It is better if operators have to carry out two distinct operations after entering data — for example, moving a cursor before pressing 'Enter'.

5.4   Data are usually written onto a disk at intervals. These should be frequent. On one plant the computer collected spot values of each instrument reading every minute and then, every five minutes, it wrote them onto a hard disk. The hard disk survived a runaway reaction and an explosion but all other data were lost. The explosion occurred towards the end of a five-minute period and nearly five minutes' data were therefore lost. The highest pressure recorded was 4 bar, although the bursting pressure of the reactor that burst was about 60 bar[41].

5.5   When computer control is introduced into a plant some operators, especially older ones, find it difficult to adapt. King suggests that the older operators are retrained first. If not, they take longer than the newer and younger operators to pick up the new techniques and lose status and prestige in their eyes. Their extensive experience and process knowledge will then not be passed on[42].

This is a convenient point to discuss the comment, sometimes heard, that computer control turns operators into morons, who have nothing to do most of the time and then cannot cope when problems arise as they have had no practice at running the plant. It is sometimes suggested that some operations should therefore be left for the operators to carry out, in order to keep them alert.

If an operation can be carried out more efficiently or reliably by a computer then it should not be left to the operators just to keep them alert; we should find other ways of doing so — such as studying training materials or plotting efficiencies, energy usage, catalyst life or similar parameters. Also, on most plants, despite computer control, operators usually have enough to keep them occupied. There are usually some instruments out of order, a valve on hand control, equipment to be prepared for maintenance, pumps to be changed over and routine inspections to be carried out.

More important than occupying the operators' time is letting them feel that they are in charge of the plant and able to intervene when they consider it necessary to do so. They should not feel that they are passive bystanders watching an automatic system that they can neither understand nor control. We should bear this in mind when designing control systems[43].

In deciding the degree of automation, remember that fully-automated plants are not necessarily the most reliable. Hunns has compared three designs for a boiler control system: one based mainly on manual control, one partly automated and one fully automated. The partly automated design was the most reliable[44].

5.6   In the traditional design of control room the operators have to move about to inspect and adjust instruments and this may help to keep them alert. In a modern control room on a computer-controlled plant, they can carry out all the inspections and adjustments from their seats. They may easily become sleepy, especially during the night shift. Little thought seems to have been given to this aspect of computer control.

At an ergonomics conference several speakers showed how work stations could be designed so that operators can reach every control without stretching or getting up. The next speaker said it would be better if they had to stretch and get up occasionally; this would keep them alert.

5.7   Confused by other alarms, an operator failed to notice a high level alarm in a vessel. The operator added some water to the vessel; the rupture disc burst and 15 tonnes of a toxic flammable gas was discharged[14]. Apart from the weakness in the design of the display, it is bad practice to allow a relief valve to discharge flammable or toxic gases or liquids to atmosphere. They should be discharged to a flare stack, scrubbing system or catchpot[45].

6.   ERRORS IN THE DATA ENTERED IN THE COMPUTER

6.1   An operator wanted to reduce the temperature on a catalytic cracker from 982°F to 980°F. Unfortunately he pressed the keys in the wrong order (908) and immediately pressed the 'Enter' key. The computer responded with impressive speed, slamming slide valves shut and causing a flow reversal along the riser. Fortunately there were no injuries and only a small fire, at a leaking joint.

Figure 1.9

During the Hazop of computer-controlled plants we should consider the results of errors in entering data. Accidental entering of wrong data can be minimized, as already stated, by requiring operators to carry out at least two operations — for example, entering figures and then moving a cursor.

Standards should be written and vendors chosen so that a computer will reject or query data or instructions that are outside specified ranges, deviate more than a specified amount from the existing value, or fail consistency tests.

6.2   On another occasion an operator was changing a feed rate from 75 to 100 gallons per minute. 1000 was entered in error; the computer opened the feed valve to the full extent, raising the pressure in the plant. There was no damage as the relief valve lifted[46]. A second line of defence, as recommended by Leveson (see item 3.1 on page 11), countered an error in the design of the software, failure to foresee and allow for an obvious slip by the operator. (Leveson was actually concerned with errors in the writing of the software rather than its design.)

6.3   An operator was asked to calculate and enter the quantities of reagents required for a batch reaction. Although not required to do so, the operator asked the foreman to check the figures. The foreman found an error. By this time a shift change had occurred, the new operator did not realize that one of the figures had been changed and used the original ones. The error was not hazardous but the batch was spoilt.

6.4   Entering the wrong data has caused aircraft accidents. A pilot set the heading in a plane's inertial navigation system as 270° instead of 027°. The plane ran out of fuel and had to land in the Brazilian jungle. 12 people were killed[47].

In 1983 a Korean Airlines aircraft strayed off course and was shot down by a Russian fighter with the loss of 269 lives. According to one theory the flight engineer made an error while entering the plane's take-off longitude into the navigation system[48]. Another theory is that the plane was moved too soon after entering its position, before it had time to 'digest' the data. If so, this incident falls into my 'black box' category (see Section 4, page 16) — the crew not understanding what goes on inside the computer and its limitations.

6.5   Errors can occur because data are entered in the wrong units. For example, a granulated material was normally passed through extruders at a rate of 2 tonnes/hr. The unit was shut down for a number of changes including some modifications to the software. After start-up the control system was still calibrated in tonnes/hr but the modified display asked for the feed rate in kilograms/hr. The operator entered 2000 and the extruder then tried to pass 2000 tonnes/hr[28].

In this case the computer asked for the data to be entered in the wrong units. Other incidents have occurred because an operator entered data in the wrong units. In one case the operator typed the code for temperature instead of the code for pressure. Rather than adjusting the pressure to 800 (mm of mercury), the computer tried to raise the temperature to 800°C[14]. The computer should have been programmed to query or reject data outside specified ranges (see item 6.1, page 29).

Two similar incidents involved aircraft. A plane became short of fuel and had to make a forced landing because x pounds of fuel were loaded instead of x kg). In the second incident two pilots of an Airbus A320 (both of whom were killed) may have intended to instruct the flight control system to descend at an angle of 3.3 degrees, but instead instructed it to descend at the very rapid rate of 3300 feet per minute. Both instructions were represented by two-figure numbers. The program has now been changed so that the speed of descent is represented by a four-figure number.

In process plants the computer can be instructed to query data which are outside specified ranges (see item 6.1, page 29), but on an aircraft it may be necessary in an emergency to select extreme values. It is possible that the crash was due to a failure of the computer system but the inquiry considered this much less likely than the reason I have described. No accident has a single cause[49] and in this case contributory causes were poor communication between the pilots (who had never flown together before), distraction by last minute changes by air traffic control, and the lack of a ground proximity warning system[12].

6.6   An operator should have moved three tonnes of water into reactor A. He misread the display and moved three tonnes into reactor B which was already full. There was a large spillage of cyanide material which affected the operator[14]. Overfilling of vessels is a frequent event and when the contents are as hazardous as cyanide they should overflow to a safe place.

This incident, like many more of those I have described, would at one time have been put down to human error. But this is superficial; the accident could have been prevented (or made less likely) by better design of the display and the effects could have been mitigated by a change in plant design. Once again we see a familiar error on a computer-controlled plant. Even when operators add material to a vessel from a bucket, they have been known to put it in the wrong one. When the task is carried out remotely, the operator is less likely to notice that the wrong vessel is being filled and will not see at once that the vessel is overflowing.

6.7   An interesting example of an error in entering data, though not in a control application, occurred while I was writing this chapter. I was communicating with the author of Chapter 3, Chaim Shen-Orr, by e-mail. I wrote each message with my word processing program and put it in an ASCII file called SHEN-ORR. On several occasions, when I tried to send this file by e-mail I got the response 'File not found'. After a few tries I gave up and faxed the message instead.

After a couple of months I found the reason for the failure. When naming the file I had typed a number 0 instead of a capital letter O. As the key for the number 0 is next to the hyphen (-) key, the error is easy to make and the two symbols look almost identical on the screen.

The error came to light when I was looking at a list of old files, which I had numbered SHEN-ORR.EM1, .EM2 and .EM3 and noted that SHEN-0RR.EM3 was at the top of the list (as numbers are listed before letters).

32

I wasted a lot of time before I solved the problem, and so did the computer services manager at Loughborough University who tried to help me. We assumed I was using an incorrect procedure and he went through the routine with me, but we used a trial file which we called ABCD! Tests should be like real life. On a control program the consequences of the wrong entry might be more serious. But no operator, asked to add 1O (one-letter-O) tonnes to a reactor would say, 'I can't add one-letter-O tonnes, there's no such thing, so I'll give up'.

A more friendly program would have asked me to select the file from a list rather than type its name. All the same, I think I'll stick to pigeons in future.

7. FAILURE TO TELL OPERATORS OF CHANGES IN DATA OR PROGRAMS

I do not know of any incidents in the process industries that have occurred because operators were not told of changes, but it has caused an aircraft accident. In 1979 the destination way-point of an Air New Zealand sightseeing flight to Antarctica was moved two degrees to the East but the crew were not told. The inertial navigation system guided the plane, which was flying low so that the passengers could see the scenery, along a valley that ended in a cliff. It looked very similar to the open-ended valley that the crew expected to follow; they did not realize they were on the wrong course and they flew into the cliffs. All 257 people on board were killed[50,51] (see Chapter 3, Section 10, page 97).

8. INTERFERENCE WITH HARDWARE OR SOFTWARE

8.1 Unauthorized interference with computer electronics is difficult, but interference with peripheral equipment may be more serious than on a traditional plant as the computer does not know that interference has occurred. For example, the leads on a limit switch on a valve were interchanged to carry out some tests. The plant was on manual control at the time but was switched back to computer control before the leads were restored to their correct positions. The computer thought the valve was open when it was shut and decided to close it. It actually opened it, releasing flammable material[9].

If the plant had been controlled conventionally then the operators involved may have known of the temporary interchange of the leads or a notice could have been placed on the panel informing them. However, it would be difficult to tell the computer that the valve is open when the signal says it is shut! A computer provides new opportunities for familiar communication errors.

This incident, like most of those described in this book, was not really the result of using a computer. It was the result of an unsatisfactory method of preparing equipment for maintenance — a frequent cause of accidents on plants of all sorts[52]. The incident could have occurred on manual control if the operator had forgotten that the switches were interchanged. Perhaps the operator had forgotten. Or perhaps the all-powerful computer was expected to know somehow what had happened. According to the report on one incident, even when alarms were sounding, the operator did not believe it was a real emergency; 'the computer can cope'. Eberts says that some operators expect computers to behave like humans and cannot understand why they make mistakes that no human would make[53] (see Chapter 3, Section 10, page 96).

A somewhat similar incident occurred during trip testing, using a new procedure still in draft form. As part of the procedure an earth (ground) lead was disconnected. A reactor temperature reading fell to zero and the temperature control loop responded accordingly. The control loop should have been put on manual but the procedure did not say so. A conventional control loop could have been left on auto, but not a computer-controlled one[14].

Another incident occurred with a hydraulically-operated paper-cutting guillotine. It was fitted with a photo-electric guard to prevent operation while paper was being loaded and, in addition, the operator had to press two buttons, one with each hand, to operate the guillotine. There were two parallel control systems, each containing six components, and failure of any component would prevent the guillotine operating. Nevertheless, the machine operated as the operator interrupted the light curtain and amputated a hand.

There had been a leak from the hydraulic valve, operated by a solenoid, which controlled the direction of movement of the guillotine blade. A maintenance technician replaced the valve but connected the wires up the wrong way round. There was no indication on the wires to show the correct method of connection. The machine failed to operate on test so the technician returned to the rear to interchange the wires. As the technician disappeared the operator approached the front of the machine and interrupted the light curtain. Because the wires were connected the wrong way round this caused the blade to move downwards instead of upwards[3].

The accident would not have occurred if:
- the design had been better. It should not have been possible to interchange the connections (interchanging hoses has caused several serious accidents[52]);
- the safety system, based on the photo-electric guard, was independent of the hydraulic control system;
- the hydraulic power supply had been made inoperative before maintenance was started;

- no-one was allowed to approach the machine while it was being maintained;
- the technician had labelled the wires before disconnecting them.

Any one of these actions would have prevented the accident.

8.2   A computer was taken off-line to revise a program. At the time it was counting the revolutions on a metering pump that was charging a batch reactor. When the computer was put back on-line it carried on counting where it had left off and the reactor was overcharged.

8.3   If an instrument reading is faulty, operators are sometimes able to override the instrument and type in an estimated reading. Sometimes they are right and production continues; sometimes they are wrong and an incident occurs[54]. Operators are usually reluctant to believe unusual readings and rush to the conclusion that the instrument is faulty, whatever the type of control.

Similarly, unauthorized changes to software can cause incidents. A reduced flow of cooling water to a condenser caused a rise in pressure in a vacuum distillation column. A software-based trip should have shut the plant down but the operator had bypassed the system by rewriting the software[14]. Changes to software should be controlled as rigidly as changes to hardware or operating instructions.

Today it is usually harder for operators to interfere with the software (or to type in 'correct' readings) than in the early days of computer control. However, some companies allow operators to have 'keys' which let them override data, change interlock settings and so on. Other operators acquire them in various ways, much as operators have always acquired various tools and adaptors that they were not supposed to have.

One company's attitude is to avoid the use of passwords and keys and instead to make anything they want the operators to do easy to carry out, and anything they do not want them to do difficult, unless they have had special training.

8.4   I have seen only one report of a virus in process control software: a newspaper reported that a virus was found in the central computer of a Lithuanian nuclear plant[55] (see Afterthoughts on page 115, last quotation).

Many control engineers believe that the viruses seen so far could not infect process control software. This does not mean, however, that virus infection will never occur (boot viruses can infect any computer), and the consequences could be much more serious than loss of accountancy data. As long as a control computer stands alone and is not connected to other systems (or is connected so that the flow of data is outwards only), infection is impossible (unless a virus is present in the original software or is introduced by a user or maintenance worker — see Chapter 3, Section 11, page 99) but networking is becoming increasingly common.

Computer viruses are rather like AIDS[56]. To avoid infection do not promiscuously share data or disks and keep the covers on your disks in the presence of computers whose background is unknown. In addition, it would be wise to check for known viruses from time to time.

9.   OTHER PROBLEMS

What new problems will occur in the future? Jones[2] is concerned that new developments may make use of expert systems and other types of artificial intelligence which involve value judgements and weighted preferences. He asks, 'Who interprets the facts?', 'On what bases are inferences drawn?', 'By what standards are values assigned?' and 'By what process are priorities set?'. Some expertise is based on experienced judgement ('gut feel') rather than facts or causal relationships. To say this is not to deny its value but it is difficult or impossible to check such expertise for accuracy or consistency[57].

Cox[58] writes, 'What happens if the [expert] system's decisions are not fulfilled but are accepted and implemented to the point of catastrophe? Who is to be held responsible?' Of course, designers and experts are always responsible for the results of their recommendations (and often try to avoid responsibility; see the quotation at the beginning of Chapter 3, page 81). With an expert system, how is responsibility shared between the expert who provides the knowledge and judgement and the knowledge engineer who incorporates them into a computer program?

A simple example may illustrate the problem. A main road near my home was dug up for repair of the water mains. Two lines of traffic, in one direction, were reduced to one. The flow through a set of traffic lights was halved and a tail-back formed. The automatic equipment noted a reduced flow, assumed there was less demand, reduced the time allowed and the tail-back got worse. (If artificial intelligence is defined as 'making machines do things that require intelligence when done by men' then this is artificial stupidity.) The consequences were trivial but where does responsibility for the incident lie? How is it shared between the road engineer and the systems analyst who between them failed to foresee the results of abnormal operating conditions and the managers who failed to encourage a systematic search for such problems? Is it any different from other failures to foresee consequences?

Downes[34] points out that computer control might produce complicated interactions ('couplings') between sections of a plant that were previously unconnected.

According to Mackenzie[12], codes and regulations cause problems in two ways: different industries or types of equipment are often subject to different codes and regulations, even though the problems are similar, and these codes and regulations are often written for traditional rather than computer-controlled equipment.

There is a need for technologists who are equally at home in the fields of process engineering and computer control. There are such people, greatly valued by their managers, but we need more and I know of no courses which set out to train them.

10. CONCLUSIONS

If we can learn from the incidents that have occurred on process plants controlled by computers we may be able to prevent them from happening again. Familiar errors caused the incidents that have occurred. Accidents or process upsets will occur in any plant if we do not allow for foreseeable slips or equipment failures, if operators are overloaded by too much information, if information display is poor, if controllers are set incorrectly, if warnings are ignored or if operators are not told of changes that have been made. However, some of these errors are more likely to occur on plants controlled by a computer than on a conventional plant, as different departments may be responsible for operation of the plant and design and operation of the computer, and operating staff may have exaggerated views of the power of the computer and a limited understanding of what it can and cannot do and how it does it.

The following are the principal recommendations that can be drawn from the incidents I have described. The numbers in brackets at the end of each paragraph refer to the items in this chapter.

• Identify foreseeable hardware failures and power supply interruptions and design so that they do not have unacceptable results (or, more precisely, so that the probability of an unacceptable result is acceptably low) (2.2).

• Safety systems such as emergency trips should be completely independent of the control system and, when practicable, hard-wired. If they are based on a computer, it should be independent of the control computer (2.2, 3.1 and 8.1). Interlocks which, for example, prevent one valve being open when another is also open, are in an intermediate category and the degree of independence should be considered in each case (2.2).

• Specify the conditions under which equipment will be used during normal

37

operation and during abnormal conditions such as start-up, shutdown and catalyst regeneration (2.3).

• Manage changes to hardware or software and the ability of operators to override readings. Before hardware or software changes take place a responsible person should carry out a systematic study of their consequences (Introduction (page 1), 3.1, 3.2.2, 8.1 and 8.3).

• Base systems software, whenever possible, on well-tested systems from reputable suppliers (3.1).

• Test all software as thoroughly as is practicable and expect this to take longer than design (3.1).

• Design plants, when possible, so that software errors will not have serious effects (3.1 and 6.2).

• Carry out hazard and operability studies (see Chapter 2) on the software logic with the applications engineer as a member of the Hazop team (4). Train operators to understand the scope and limitations of the system (4.5 and 8.1).

• Avoid blanket instructions; instead ask what the computer should do for all deviations at all stages of a batch process (4.1) and what will be the results of foreseeable instrument and measurement failures (4.3).

• Look for ambiguities in the software logic. For example, an applications engineer asked to keep an output steady may keep a valve position steady instead of keeping the flow or temperature steady (4.1).

• When possible, simplify designs instead of relying on trips and interlocks. Remember that the lifetime cost of an instrument is about twice the cost of purchase and installation (4.4).

• Do not omit or rush Hazops on seemingly simple systems (4.4).

• Consider the need for the computer to warn operators when readings are unusual, inconsistent, drifting or 'stuck', inconsistent with mass balances or have reached the full-scale deflection of the measuring instrument. Train operators to look through the display pages from time to time. Show the time on display pages (4.3, 4.4 and 4.6).

• Do not overload operators with too many alarms (5.1).

• Display together the information needed for dealing with each alarm (5.1).

• Do not let all the display pages look alike (5.2).

• Do not give function keys different functions on different pages (5.2).

• Display data required by operators and that required only by technical staff on different pages (5.2).

• Encourage operators to check data and instructions — for example, by requiring them to carry out two distinct operations when entering data (5.3).

• Write data on hard disks at frequent intervals (5.4).

• Remember that the older operators, who find it hardest to adapt to computer control, may know more about the process than the younger ones and that their knowledge and experience are valuable (5.5).

● Design systems so that operators feel they are in charge, not watching something they cannot understand or control (5.5).

● Consider ways of keeping operators alert during quiet shifts (5.5 and 5.6).

● Design displays so that important data are easily recognized (5.7).

● Program computers to reject or query data or instructions that are outside specified ranges, deviate more than a specified amount from the current value or fail consistency tests. During Hazops, consider the effects of inputting wrong data (6.1, 6.2 and 6.5).

● Do not use more than one system of units (for example, bars and psi) but, if you have to (for example, because tonnes of one material are added to a reactor but only kilogrammes of another), enter the units when entering data (6.5).

● Tell operators when data or programs are changed (7).

● Do not allow equipment to be taken off-line or maintained without the agreement and understanding of the process team (8.1 and 8.2).

● Look for differences in performance between conventional and computer-controlled systems (8.1).

● Design equipment so that it cannot be assembled incorrectly (8.1).

● De-energize equipment before maintaining it (8.1).

● Do not allow unauthorized disks or signals to be connected to computers (8.4).

● Check for known viruses from time to time (8.4).

● Train a number of engineers so that they are equally at home in the fields of process engineering and computer control (9).

● Publicize the incidents that occur on your plants so that others can learn from them (see Preface).

Remember:

● computers provide new and easier opportunities for making familiar errors;

● people can do what we want them to do; computers can do only what we tell them to do.

11.   APPENDIX: SOME ADDITIONAL CONTROL FUNCTIONS THAT COMPUTERS MIGHT UNDERTAKE

This section suggests two additional tasks which computers might be programmed to undertake. They involve an additional level of complexity compared with the control functions that are carried out already.

11.1   DRAWING ATTENTION TO HAZARDS

This is best illustrated by an example. If hot oil, over 100°C, is added to a storage tank containing a water layer, or the oil in the tank is heated above 100°C, the water may be vaporized with explosive violence; a mixture of steam and oil will be expelled through the tank vent and may even blow the roof off the tank. Structures tens of metres tall may be covered with black oil. The phenomenon, known as foam-over or froth-over, is well known but nevertheless continues to happen. So many things can go wrong that an operator can hardly be fully aware of them all, though once the operator is prompted, they may be recalled. Newton[59] suggests that if the temperature of the incoming oil or the oil in the tank approaches 100°C then the screen could display a warning message, not merely announcing a high temperature but reminding the operator of the consequences. The reminder message could also be displayed if the operator starts up or increases the heat supply to a tank which contains a water layer.

The number of possible incidents that might occur and warnings that might be given is enormous and each plant would have to make a selection based on its own experience and that of the industry, as described in publications such as References 60 and 61. There might be a market for a collection of triggering events and warning messages, from which each plant could make its selection. A 'Help' function could explain why the consequences may occur and refer the operator to a plant instruction, accident report or other document for more information. These documents and perhaps the whole of References 59 and 60 could be accessible on the screen.

11.2   PREPARATION FOR MAINTENANCE

When equipment has to be handed over to the maintenance organization for repair, the operating team usually prepare the equipment by isolating it from other equipment that is still in use, removing hazardous materials and labelling it so that the right equipment is worked on. A permit-to-work is issued by the operating team and accepted by the maintenance team. The permit describes the work to be done, any remaining hazards and the precautions necessary. Many accidents have occurred because the procedure was poor or was not followed.

Newton[59] suggests that permits-to-work could be prepared and stored on a computer. The saving in effort would not be great but additional functions are now possible. For example:

• the computer could remind the user of any special hazards associated with this piece of equipment and its contents and the actions that should be taken; it could also bring up any points highlighted during the Hazop;

• the computer could also remind the user of any problems encountered when the equipment was being prepared or maintained on earlier occasions;

- if a vessel is being prepared for entry, the computer could check that the number of slip-plates (blinds) to be fitted (or pipes disconnected) is the same as the number of connections shown on the drawing;
- if someone tries to take out a second permit on the same item of equipment, this would be instantly apparent, and the computer could refuse to issue it;
- suppose a fitter has to replace a gasket during a night shift. On some plants it is easy; only one sort is used and all the fitter has to do is select the right size. On other plants many types are used. The fitter has to get out a line diagram, find the line number and then look up the details in a bulky equipment list. It should be possible to view the line diagram on a computer screen, select the line with a cursor and have details of the line displayed, including the location of spare parts and any distinguishing marks such as the colour of the gaskets. The line diagram and equipment list will have been prepared on a computer; all that is needed is a link between the design system and the maintenance system. (Of course, we should, if possible, reduce the number of types of gaskets, nuts and bolts, etc, required even though we may use more expensive types than strictly necessary on some duties.)

The issue of permits-to-work is a job for an off-line computer, not the process control one, but it could be linked to the maintenance information system and equipment list. STEP (Standard for Exchange of Product Model Data or ISO 10303) and the process industries version (PISTEP) may make it easier to do this.

In both of these tasks the programs, like all those intended for plant use, should be friendly. They should not, like so many programs, refuse to recognize a name such as 'blowdown' because the operator types 'blow-down'.

AN AFTERTHOUGHT
In this chapter, as in many of my books, I have tried to remind readers of some of the lessons of the past so that they will not repeat them in the future.

'And when will this mission be accomplished? ...
When my hour comes
I'll leave behind
perhaps an echo
for man, who forgets
and remembers and starts again.'
Edith Bruck (Italian poet, b. 1932)

41

REFERENCES IN CHAPTER 1

1. Kletz, T.A., 1992, *Hazop and Hazan — Identifying and Assessing Process Industry Hazards*, 3rd edition (Institution of Chemical Engineers, Rugby, UK).
2. Jones, P.G., 1991, Computers in chemical plant — a need for safety awareness, *Hazards XI — New Directions in Process Safety, Symposium Series No. 124* (Institution of Chemical Engineers, Rugby, UK).
3. Ward, G.R. and Jeffs, A.R., October 1994, Out of control — the anatomy of control system failure, *Safety and Reliability Society Symposium, Altrincham, UK*.
4. Lowe, D.R.T., 1984, *Measurement and Control*, 17: 317.
5. Bucher, W. and Fretz, R., 1986, Safety aspects of computer-controlled chemical plants, *Proceedings of the Fifth International Symposium on Loss Prevention and Safety Promotion in the Process Industries*, Volume 2 (Société de Chimie Industrielle, Paris, France).
6. Wray, A.M., 1986, *Design for Safe Operation — Experimental Rig to Production* (Institute of University Safety Officers, Bristol, UK), 36.
7. Health and Safety Executive, 1987, *Programmable Electronic Systems in Safety Related Applications* (Her Majesty's Stationery Office, London). For a summary see Pearson, J. and Brazendale, J., 1988, *Preventing Major Chemical and Process Related Accidents, Symposium Series No. 110* (Institution of Chemical Engineers, Rugby, UK), 195. For an example of industry-specific advice see 1994, *Programmable Electronic Equipment in Safety-Related Applications (Safety Recommendations — IGE/SR/15)* (Institution of Gas Engineers, London). See also 1990, *Safe IT (Information Technology): Vol 1, Overall Approach, Vol 2, Standards Framework* (Health and Safety Executive, London).
8. Kletz, T.A., 1982, *Plant/Operations Progress*, 1 (4): 209.
9. Eddershaw, B.W., 1989, *Loss Prevention Bulletin*, 088: 3.
10. Smith, A., November 1987, *Processing*, p. 47.
11. Forester, T. and Morrison, P., 1990, *Futures*, 22: 462.
12. MacKenzie, D., 1994, *Science and Public Policy*, 21 (4): 233.
13. Nimmo, I., Nunns, S.R. and Eddershaw, B.W., November 1987, Lessons learned from the failure of computer system controlling a nylon polymer plant, *Safety and Reliability Society Symposium, Altrincham, UK*.
14. Nimmo, I., 1994, *Chemical Engineering Progress*, 90 (10): 32.
15. Franke, L.F. and Zodeh, O.M., 1991, *Plant/Operations Progress*, 10 (2): 93.
16. Borning, A., 1987, *Communications of the Association for Computing Machinery (ACM)*, 30 (2).
17. Sankaran, S., May 1987, Applying computers to safe control and operation of hazardous process plants, *Instrument Asia 87 Conference, Singapore*.
18. Wray, A.M., 1988, *New Scientist*, 119: 61.
19. Taylor, J.R., October 1994, Safety assessment of control systems — the impact of computer control, *Israel Institute for Petroleum and Energy Conference on Process Safety Management, Tel Aviv, Israel*.
20. Gondran, M., October 1986, Launch meeting of the European Safety and Reliability

Association, Brussels, Belgium.
21. Leveson, N.G., 1990, *IEEE Software*, 7 (6): 55.
22. Kletz, T.A., 1991, *Plant Design for Safety — A User-Friendly Approach* (Hemisphere, New York).
23. US Department of Energy, 1989, *Errors in Commercial Software Increase Potential for Process Piping Failures, Bulletin No 89–B.*
24. Andow, P.K., 1992, private communication.
25. Boettcher, D., 1994, *Atom*, 433: 34.
26. Welsh, R., 1994, *Atom*, 433: 39.
27. Leveson, N.G. and Turner, C.S., 1993, *IEEE Computer*, 26 (7): 18.
28. Institution of Chemical Engineers, 1994, *Slide Training Package No. 025: Modifications: the Management of Change* (Institution of Chemical Engineers, Rugby, UK), item 5.6.
29. Berry, A., 1 May 1993, *The Daily Telegraph.*
30. Chemical Industries Association, 1985, *Chemical Safety Summary*, 56 (221): 6 (Chemical Industries Association, London).
31. Bergroth, K., 1992, Explosion in a sulphonation process, *7th International Symposium on Loss Prevention and Safety Promotion in the Process Industries, Taormina, Italy*, Volume 1 (SRP Partners, Rome).
32. Kletz, T.A., 1991, *An Engineer's View of Human Error*, 2nd edition (Institution of Chemical Engineers, Rugby, UK), 10.
33. Englund, S.M. and Grinwis, D.J., 1992, *Chemical Engineering Progress*, 88 (10): 36.
34. Downes, A.M., 1991, private communication.
35. Garner, P., 1983, *Rube Goldberg — A Retrospect* (Putnam, New York).
36. Heath Robinson, W., 1973, *Inventions* and 1974, *Railway Ribaldry* (Duckworth, London).
37. Edwards, E. and Lees, F.P., 1973, *Man and Computers in Process Control* (Institution of Chemical Engineers, Rugby, UK), 159.
38. Bodsberg, L. and Ingstad, O., 1989, Technical and human implications of automatic safety systems, *6th International Symposium on Loss Prevention and Safety Promotion in the Process Industries, Oslo, Norway*, Volume 1.
39. Shaw, J.A., 1990, Design your distributed control system to reduce operator error, *AIChE Loss Prevention Symposium, San Diego, CA, USA.*
40. Embrey, D.E., 1994, *Guidelines for Preventing Human Error in Process Safety* (AIChE, New York), Chapter 7.
41. Mooney, D.G., 1991, An overview of the Shell fluoroaromatics explosion, *Hazards XI — New Directions in Process Safety, Symposium Series No. 124* (Institution of Chemical Engineers, Rugby, UK).
42. King, D.W., 1983, *Plant/Operations Progress*, 2 (1): 73 (discussion).
43. Love, J., 1984, *The Chemical Engineer*, 403: 17.
44. Hunns, D.M., 1981, *Terotechnica*, 2: 159.
45. Kletz, T.A., 1994, *What Went Wrong — Case Histories of Process Plant Disasters*, 3rd edition (Gulf Publishing, Houston, TX, USA), section 10.4.6.

46. Lorenzo, D.K., 1990, *A Manager's Guide to Reducing Human Errors* (Chemical Manufacturers Association, Washington, DC, USA), 18.
47. Learmont, D., January 1990, *Flight International*, 42.
48. 1 September 1986, *Time*, p. 24.
49. Kletz, T.A., 1994, *Learning from Accidents*, 2nd edition (Butterworth-Heinemann, Oxford, UK).
50. Mahon, P., 1984, *Verdict on Erebus* (Collins, Auckland, New Zealand).
51. Shadbolt, M., November 1984, *Readers Digest*, 164–200.
52. Kletz, T.A., 1994, *What Went Wrong — Case Histories of Process Plant Disasters* (Gulf Publishing Company, Houston, TX, USA), Chapter 1.
53. Eberts, R.E., 1985, *Chemical Engineering Progress*, 81 (12): 30.
54. Gabbett, J.F., 1982, PVC computer control experience, *AIChE Loss Prevention Symposium, Anaheim, CA, USA*.
55. Lüfkens, M., 3 February 1992, *The Daily Telegraph*.
56. Becket, M., 26 September 1989, *The Daily Telegraph*.
57. Institution of Chemical Engineers, 1987, *The Engineer's Responsibility for Computer Based Decisions* (Institution of Chemical Engineers, Rugby, UK), 11.
58. Cox, S., 1994, *Stress and Work*, 1 (1): 6.
59. Newton, A.M., 1995, *Journal of Loss Prevention in the Process Industries*, 8 (1): 41.
60. Kletz, T.A., 1994, *What Went Wrong — Case Histories of Process Plant Disasters*, 3rd edition (Gulf Publishing, Houston, TX, USA).
61. *Loss Prevention Bulletin*, published bi-monthly by the Institution of Chemical Engineers, Rugby, UK.

2. HAZARD AND OPERABILITY (HAZOP) STUDIES APPLIED TO COMPUTER-CONTROLLED PROCESS PLANTS

Paul Chung and Eamon Broomfield

*'There is a strong family resemblance about misdeeds, and if you
have all the details of a thousand at your finger ends, it is odd if you
can't unravel the thousand and first.'*
Sherlock Holmes in *A Study in Scarlet* by Arthur Conan Doyle

1. INTRODUCTION

Due to the speed and flexibility of computers, there is an increasing use of software in industry to control or manage systems that are safety-critical. In some cases, as systems become more and more complex, and faster and faster response time is required, the use of computer and application software is the only feasible approach. In this chapter a safety-critical system refers to a system which, if it malfunctions, may cause injury to people, loss of life or serious damage to property. To ensure the quality of safety-critical systems with software components, standards and guidelines have been, or are being, produced by government and professional organizations[1-7].

The guidance generally given is that software quality is achieved through rigorous management of the software life cycle which involves requirement analysis, specification, design, implementation, testing, verification and validation. Safety assessment is a new dimension which needs to be added to the life cycle of safety-critical software. For example, the draft *Defence Standard 00–56: Safety Management Requirements for Defence Systems Containing Programmable Electronics*[6] states that, 'The contractor shall identify hazards and their associated accident sequences, calculate safety targets for each hazard and assess the system to determine whether the safety targets have been met'. Although safety assessment has been accepted as an important part of the software life cycle, little help is given to engineers about when and how to do it. Safety assessment involves two different activities: hazard identification and hazard analysis. The aim of the former is to identify the potential hazards that may arise from the use of a particular safety-critical system, and their possible causes. The aim of the latter is to quantify the risks that are associated with the identified hazards and to assess whether the risks are acceptable. The focus of this chapter is on hazard identification.

45

In the process industry, Hazop (hazard and operability studies)[8,9] is a long-established methodology used for identifying hazards in chemical plant design. Some attempts have been made to modify conventional Hazop for computer-related systems. Modified versions of Hazop are generally referred to as Chazop (computer Hazop) or PES (programmable electronic systems) Hazop in the literature.

In this chapter we provide a brief description of the conventional Hazop as used in the process industry and an overview of the different Chazop frameworks/guidelines suggested by engineers and researchers over the past few years. The overview shows that there is as yet no agreed format on how Chazop should be done and that the different approaches were made *ad hoc*. The main emphasis of the rest of the chapter is on a new Chazop methodology[10] which we have systematically developed and which is based on incident analysis. We discuss the strategy used to develop the methodology and illustrate the application of the methodology using examples.

2. COMPUTER-RELATED HAZARDS

Hazards are sometimes caused by system failures, or by systems deviating from their intended behaviour. System failures can be categorized into two classes[3]:

• random failures typically result from normal breakdown mechanisms in hardware; the reliability based on failure rate can often be predicted in a quantified statistical manner with reasonable accuracy;

• systematic failures are all those failures which cause a system to fail, and which are not due to random failures.

McDermid[11] has pointed out that, 'software is quite different to hardware in that its only "failure mode" is through design or implementation faults, rather than any form of physical mechanism such as ageing'. Therefore, all software-induced system failures are systematic failures. 'There is some evidence that as the level of complexity [of a system] increases the proportion of systematic failures increases'[3].

However, a piece of software in itself is not hazardous. It is hazardous only when it interacts with equipment that can cause injury to people, loss of life or damage to property. Therefore safety-critical software should, as far as possible, be:

• able to respond to external failures, hardware or human, in an appropriate manner. This means that the design specification should have no omissions, and every conceivable problem should be considered and dealt with accordingly;

• free from error, so that it will not make any wrong decisions and cause wrong actions to be taken.

An ideal hazard identification methodology, therefore, should be able to deal with system design/specification, software implementation and maintenance.

3.   HAZOP

Hazop[8,9] is a methodology developed by ICI in the 1960s for reviewing chemical plant designs. A Hazop team should consist of a leader who controls the discussion and members from the production, technical and engineering departments. This is to ensure that the required expertise for reviewing a particular design is present at the meeting. The team has an engineering line diagram (ELD) in front of them and the general intention of the system is explained. To help the team go through the design in a systematic manner, members review the design section by section, or line by line. Guide words are used as prompts to help them explore possible causes and consequences of deviations from design intent. For example, the guide words include: *none, more of* and *less of*. The deviations associated with the guide word *none* are *no flow* and *reverse flow*. The team then consider questions such as *What will cause no flow along this line?* and *What will cause low level in this tank?* If the cause of a particular deviation is credible and the consequence is believed to be significant then a change is made to the design or method of operation, or the problem is considered in detail outside the Hazop meeting. An action may specify that protective equipment needs to be installed, or detailed analysis of the cause and consequence needs to be carried out. Thus a Hazop meeting generates a report in the format shown in Table 2.1 on page 48.

This conventional form of Hazop is carried out when the ELD of a design is completed. However, delaying hazard studies until the ELD is available means that many major design decisions will have been made and orders will have been placed. Therefore, changes made at this stage can be very costly. For this reason ICI introduced two preliminary hazard studies prior to the ELD stage (which is referred to as Study 3)[12]. The purpose of Study 1 is to ensure 'that the hazardous properties of all the materials involved in the process and their potential interactions are understood'. Study 2 is carried out when the process flow diagrams are available. The sections making up the plant — for example, reaction, scrubbing, distillation, etc — are studied in turn. The approach used is to consider 'top events', potential hazardous events such as fire, explosion and so on, and to 'identify those which present a serious hazard, so that an appropriate design can be developed'.

ICI later added Hazard Studies 4 to 6. Prior to plant start-up, Study 4 is done by the plant or commissioning manager to check that all actions from previous studies have been carried out and to review that appropriate procedures

TABLE 2.1

Conventional Hazop table

Guide word	Deviation	Possible causes	Consequences	Action required
None	No flow	....	....	....
	Reverse flow	....	....	....
More	More flow	....	....	....
	More pressure	....	....	....
	More temperature	....	....	....
	More level	....	....	....
Less	*(similar to more)*	....	....	....
Part of	Concentration	....	....	....
Other	Maintenance	....	....	....
	Start-up	....	....	....
	Shutdown	....	....	....
	Extra constituent or phase	....	....	....
	....	....	....	....

for operating the plant are in place. Study 5 involves a site inspection, paying particular attention to means of access and escape, guarding, provision of emergency equipment, etc. Study 6 reviews changes made during commissioning of the plant.

An earlier study (Hazard Study 0) is now being introduced. It is carried out at the start of a project, before the engineering design department is involved, and asks if the right product is being made by the most suitable route and in the most suitable location.

Two related hazard identification techniques — FMEA (Failure Modes and Effects Analysis)[13] and FMECA (Failure Modes Effects and Criticality Analysis) — will also be referred to later in this chapter. In contrast to Hazop, FMEA and FMECA represent a 'bottom up' approach to hazard identification. They start by focusing on a component and then address the questions:
● what are the modes of failure (that is, what equipment can fail and in which way)?

48

- what are the causes of the failures?
- what are the consequences?

FMECA goes further then FMEA by considering the questions 'How critical are the consequences?' and 'How often does the failure occur?'.

4.   COMPUTER HAZOP

As mentioned earlier, because of the successful application and widespread use of Hazop in the process industry, researchers and engineers are suggesting ways of adapting Hazop to safety-critical systems. This section describes the results of some of these adaptations of Hazop. The description is brief. It highlights the different guide words and questions proposed under different schemes to assist the hazard identification process during Chazop meetings. Interested readers should refer to the original articles referenced throughout the section. A general discussion about the different schemes is given at the end of the section.

4.1   SCHEME 1

An obvious way of developing a Chazop methodology is to simply replace or supplement the process-related guide words and deviations with computer-related ones. Burns and Pitblado[14] have identified two sets of guide words for reviewing computer control systems. One set is for considering the hardware and logic of the system (see Table 2.2), and the other is for considering human factors (see Table 2.3 on page 50).

TABLE 2.2
PES Hazop guide words and deviations (after Burns and Pitblado[14])

Guide word	Deviation
No	No signal
	No action
More	More signal
	More action
Less	Less signal
	Less action
Wrong	Wrong signal
	Wrong action

TABLE 2.3

Human factors Hazop guide words and deviations (after Burns and Pitblado[14])

Guide word	Deviation
No	No information
	No action
More	More information
Less	Less information
Wrong	Wrong action

The draft guideline for Chazop produced by the UK Ministry of Defence[7] extends the list of guide words associated with conventional Hazop with the following words: *early*, *late*, *before* and *after*. The words *early* and *late* are for considering actions or events relative to time and the words *before* and *after* are for considering the ordering of actions or events.

During a Chazop meeting a team will go through a diagrammatic representation of a system by considering all the links between different components on the diagram. Possible deviations from design intent are investigated by systematically applying the guide words to attributes such as *data flow, control flow, data rate, data value, event, action, repetition time, response time* and *encoding*.

Not all combinations of guide words and attributes are meaningful. The guideline recommends that 'inappropriate guide words should be removed from the study list during the planning stage' and 'the interpretations of all attribute/guide word combinations should be defined and documented by the study leader'. At the discretion of the study leader, new guide words may also be added.

Fink *et al*[15] have devised a set of application-specific guide words and deviations. The application is a clinical laboratory information system where patient test details are kept. Access to the system is provided via computer terminals, and it is interfaced to computers which control large capacity analysers (7000 tests/hr). Patient information, including patient identity and test request code, is entered into the system and sent to the analysers. Each sample tube also has a label identifying the patient from whom the sample was drawn.

The guide words used for the Chazop of this system were: *no, not, more, less, as well as, part of, other than, sooner, later, where else, interrupt, reverse*, *more often* and *less often*. Example deviations for the guide word *no* are *no label* and *no operating*. Chazop was used to consider complex and interrelated procedures. A complementary technique, FMECA, was used to consider individual component failures.

4.2 SCHEME 2

In developing guidelines for carrying out Chazop on computer-controlled plants, Andow's approach[16] is that a Chazop methodology should have the essential ingredients of the 'traditional' Hazop but need not stick rigidly to the format. The ingredients identified as essential are:
- inter-disciplinary team must carry out the study;
- the methodology must be based on questions;
- the methodology must be systematic.

Andow suggests that Chazop should be done in two stages: preliminary and full. The purpose of a preliminary Chazop is to identify early in design critical factors that influence the overall architecture and functionality of the system; it should be carried out as part of an early Hazop. He recommends that the following be considered at the early stage:
- the proposed architecture of the system;
- safety-related functions;
- system failure;
- failure of power and other services.

The full Chazop is to evaluate the design in detail at a later stage. The team should consider three different aspects of the system:
- computer system/environment;
- input/output (I/O) signals;
- complex control schemes.

A short list of headings and/or questions is provided for each aspect (see Tables 2.4, 2.5 and 2.6 on pages 52 and 53).

4.3 SCHEME 3

Lear[17] suggests a Chazop scheme for computer control systems which is similar to Andow's full Chazop. In Lear's scheme the three top level concerns are:
- hardware;
- continuous control;
- sequence control.

In this scheme guide words used for hardware include short- and long-term power supply failure. It also suggests using the check-list published by the UK Health and Safety Executive[3]. Examples of guide words/questions relating

TABLE 2.4

Headings and questions relating to computer system/environment (after Andow[16])

Failure	Hardware	Question
Gross	Whole machine	What should happen?
		Will the operator know?
		What should he do?
		Will the failure propagate to other machines?
		Any changes needed?
Random	Cabinets, crates, etc	*(similar to whole machine)*
	Controller, I/O cards	*(similar to whole machine)*
	Communication links	*(similar to whole machine)*
	Operator consoles	*(similar to whole machine)*
	Power supplies	*(similar to whole machine)*
	Watchdog timers	*(similar to whole machine)*
	Other utilities	*(similar to whole machine)*

TABLE 2.5

Headings and questions relating to input/output signals (after Andow[16])

Signal/actuator	Deviation	Question
Signal	Low	Does it matter?
		Will the operator know?
		Any action required by the operator or other systems?
		Any changes needed?
	High	*(similiar to deviation low)*
	Invariant	*(similiar to deviation low)*
	Drifting	*(similiar to deviation low)*
	Bad	*(similiar to deviation low)*
Actuator	Driven/failure high	*(similar to signal deviation low)*
	Driven/failure low	*(similar to signal deviation low)*
	Stuck	*(similar to signal deviation low)*
	Drifting	*(similar to signal deviation low)*

TABLE 2.6

Considerations relating to complex control schemes (after Andow[16])

Scheme consideration	Aspects to be considered
Purpose and method of operation	Safety-related functions
I/O signals used	
Points of operator access	Set-points, cascades that may be made or broken, etc
Limits applied	Careful use of limits gives a good safeguard and/or early warning
Interaction with other schemes	Start-up, normal operation, shutdown. Synchronization and timing issues. Expected or required operator actions.
Controller tuning	Initialization and wind-up
Relationships with trips and alarms	
Action in the event of major plant upsets	Loss of utilities. Spurious or correct operation of emergency shutdown valves.
Protection against unauthorized modifications	
Other	Spreading a large scheme over more than one controller file

to continuous control and sequence control are shown in Tables 2.7 and 2.8 on page 54.

4.4   SCHEME 4

The Chazop framework used by Nimmo *et al*[18] for reviewing process plant design also highlighted three aspects for consideration:

- hardware;
- software interactions;
- the effect software has on the process.

In this scheme, the first stage is to carry out a conventional Hazop on a plant design, treating the computer as a 'black box' (see Chapter 1, item 4.1, page 17). The next stage is to re-trace the process route taking into account concerns from the first stage but this time concentrating on determining how the

TABLE 2.7

Considerations for continuous control (after Lear[17])

System	Consideration
Input/output parameters	Bad measurement
	Transmitter accuracy
	Conditioning
Tuning parameters	Correct?
	Change in process conditions
Entire loop	Control philosophy
	Safety-related
	Performance
Overall system	Interaction
	Order of tuning/implementation
	Training

TABLE 2.8

Considerations for sequence control (after Lear[17])

Review stage	Consideration
Overall operation	Files/reports
	What (de)activates the sequence?
	Communications
Start-up module	Is operator interaction required?
	Any areas of critical timing?
	Major equipment interactions
Running module	*(similar to start-up)*
Shutdown module	*(similar to start-up)*
Step (a small number of flow chart symbols)	*(similar to start-up)*
Final overview	Testing
	Display of sequence to operator
	Training

software will respond under different circumstances. The third stage is to consider how the software achieves its control actions. The software is divided into major areas such as sequence control, continuous control, operator conversations and data links. Key enquiries in the second and third stages revolve around such questions as:

- how will the computer know what it has to do or has already done?
- how sensitive is the level of input or output to transmission of the correct action?
- what are the potential interactions?

Nimmo[19] also provides several lists of topics for discussion in a series of Chazop meetings. The discussion topics are listed under the following headings: the overall plant, the safety backup system, instrumentation and the PES.

4.5   DISCUSSION

Ideas on how Chazop should be done are still evolving. A consensus view that is emerging is that a Chazop methodology requires a 'total' system view. Software cannot be considered in isolation. The work by Burns and Pitblado[14] emphasizes the need to assess the logic of the system and also human factors; Fink et al[15] couple Chazop with FMECA; the frameworks suggested by the other authors also include hardware, software and the environment in which they operate.

The main strength of conventional Hazop is that it facilitates systematic exploratory thinking. The use of guide words and deviations prompts the team to think of hazards which they would otherwise have missed. However, up to now, attempts made by researchers and engineers to create various Chazop schemes and to derive guide words/headings and questions are rather ad hoc. Some guide words, headings or questions are obvious as they appear in different schemes. On the other hand, it is not clear why some are included and why some are left out. It is difficult to assess the relative merits of the different schemes as there is very little experience in applying them. The relevance of various guide words or questions will only become evident through practical applications.

An overview of the above schemes shows that there are different methods of generating and grouping guide words/deviations and questions. Scheme 1 follows very closely the format of conventional Hazop. The procedure is based on selecting interconnections in the design representation. However, it concentrates on identifying hazards rather than operability problems. New guide words and computing-related attributes are proposed. It is recognized that the combinations of some of the guide words/attributes may not be meaningful or may be ambiguous. On the other hand, application-specific attributes are not likely to be useful in general because safety-critical systems can be very varied.

Schemes 2 and 3 group guide words and questions according to the general categories of hardware, software, input/output and other considerations. This approach attempts to cover the total system separately. It is very important, however, to understand and consider the interactions between different system components in order to identify hazards in a complex safety-critical system. This approach falls short in this respect.

Scheme 4 makes a strong distinction between hardware and software. However, the strength of this scheme is that the assessment procedure is geared towards understanding how the computer will respond to a process deviation and how the computer will control and affect the process. This scheme provides an interesting way of linking Chazop with conventional Hazop for the process industry. The problem is that the Chazop scheme as outlined cannot be applied in the early stages of the design process to identify any potential problems.

Instead of trying to synthesize a new scheme by merging different schemes or by modifying a particular scheme, in the next section we consider the systematic development of a new Chazop methodology based on incident analysis. Our aim is to develop a general Chazop methodology that will apply to different industrial sectors. Past incidents provide us with a wealth of information on what can go wrong with safety-critical systems. Our basic premise is that this information can be organized to provide a structured framework for considering future applications.

5. A METHODOLOGY BASED ON INCIDENT ANALYSIS

5.1   INCIDENT ANALYSIS

Although industries record incidents, there is no established method of using these incidents to identify hazards at a generic level in re-engineering old systems or developing new systems. The strategy used was to analyse computer-related incident data and use the analysis as a means of deriving a generic hazard identification methodology (see Figure 2.1). For a given incident, the approach was to derive a set of questions, based on why an incident occurred and what questions could have been asked in the first place to prevent it, and then to generalize these questions to build a methodology. The methodology derived could be incorporated into a project life cycle for use by a developer and thereby prevent the recurrence of the same or similar incidents.

Over 300 incidents were provided by two major organizations — one involved in the process industries, the other in avionics. These incident reports are very brief. No user requirements, functional specifications, architecture diagrams or software codes were provided for any of the incidents. This might at

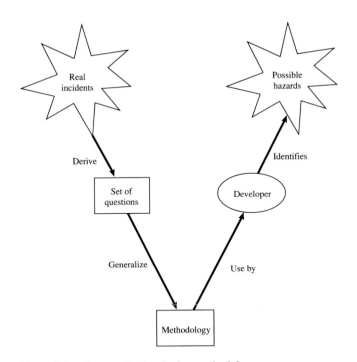

Figure 2.1   Strategy for developing methodology.

first appear to be a disadvantage. However, it forces the decomposition of the system in a general manner thereby preventing the methods developed from becoming application-specific. The process industry data, which provided very little detail, were useful for the original preliminary classification whilst the avionics data were useful for deeper analysis.

An example of one of the process industry incidents is shown in Table 2.9. An incident was caused by a control sequence which started prematurely. The sequence was started prematurely because the preconditions for starting the

TABLE 2.9
Example incident record from the process industry

Observed effect	Root cause	Cause category
Sequence started prematurely	Sequence permissives incomplete	Application software

TABLE 2.10

Example incident record from the avionics industry

A/C type	Flight phase	Location	Date	Occnum
XXX	Cruise	XXX	XXX	XXX

FMS malfunction in cruise at FL350 a/c nosed over lost 600 ft in 5 sec.
Departing altitude due to the loss of air data reference power caused by a faulty one amp circuit breaker.

sequence were not completely specified. Relevant questions that could have been asked, ideally at the specification stage rather than after the software had been designed or implemented, are:

- how is the task initiated?
- what are the preconditions for initiation?
- is the preconditions set sufficient?
- how is the task prevented from being initiated unintentionally?

Table 2.10 is an example of one of the incidents from the avionics industry. A flight management system (FMS) malfunction caused the aircraft to drop 600 ft in height. The malfunction was caused by a fault in a one amp circuit breaker which led to acceptance of invalid data.

Some useful questions that can be derived from this incident are:

- is the data update frequency sufficient?
- over what ranges are the expected values?
- is there any method of verifying or correlating input data to detect erroneous values?
- is a continual self-test sequence required?
- what are the consequences of erroneous data?
- is one sensor sufficient for this task?
- if multiple sensors are required, what strategy will be adopted for handling differences between them?
- are independent power supplies required?

Incident analysis provides us with an appreciation of what can go wrong with a safety-critical system. Furthermore, it provides a useful way of identifying questions that need to be considered during the specification, design and implementation stages. The effectiveness of a methodology depends on how representative the incidents are, and on the methods used in deriving, generalizing and grouping the questions.

5.2   GENERIC TASKS

As the analysis of incidents progressed, it became necessary to find a way of grouping the questions so that incidents within the same industry and across both industries could be related. In developing a structured framework we use a generic task approach. A system can be broken down into a number of sub-components and each of the sub-components can be mapped to a component class. Each component is responsible for carrying out a generic task (see Table 2.11). Figure 2.2 (see page 60) is a model showing the relationship between tasks and components, and also the relationships between tasks. The tasks are organized into levels which indicate how they interact. All components associated with the intervention level that interact with the computer must use some component at the I/O level. Similarly, all components associated with the I/O level that interact with the computer must involve some component at the communication level.

The model can be used to establish 'what if' scenarios. For example, if an operator inputs incorrect data, what happens if the error propagates through to the inner levels? In the worst case, the operator error causes a failure at the control and processing level. Software and hardware are so closely interlinked in many incidents that separation tends to complicate rather than simplify analysis, so both are integrated in the model.

The functional model formed the basis for unifying the causes of incidents from both industries and for classifying these causes. Incidents and associated questions were mapped into this functional model. For instance, the

TABLE 2.11
Components and generic tasks

Component class	Generic task
Utility	Intervention
Operator	Intervention
Sensor	Input
Human input device	Input
Actuator	Output
Display	Output
Communication link	Communication
Computer	Control and processing

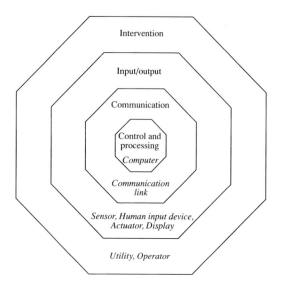

Figure 2.2   Model showing basic components and functional levels.

process industries incident described and its associated questions were mapped into the control and processing task. The questions derived from the avionics industry were mapped into different tasks. For example, the question 'Over what ranges are the expected values?' would be mapped to the I/O task, and the question 'Are independent power supplies required?' would be mapped to the intervention task.

5.3   TASK ATTRIBUTES

So far we have described how questions can be derived from incidents and how both questions and incidents can be mapped into a model of tasks. In order to refine the mapping between tasks and questions, a task is considered under five headings ('considerations') and associated with each heading is a set of attributes/guide words. Table 2.12 shows the structure for the intervention task. The headings and attributes are the same for all the generic tasks. However, the questions and incidents are not all the same.

The attributes were derived from the questions which in turn were derived from incidents. The link between question and incident is retained for two reasons. First, it illustrates why a certain question needs to be asked. Second, it gives access to previous experiences. When carrying out hazard identification on a system, the attributes may be used on their own or in conjunction with the questions and incidents which provide clarification and information on past experiences.

TABLE 2.12
Task structure

Task	Task consideration	Task attributes	Questions	Incidents
Intervention	Specification	Definition	....	....
		Objective	....	....
		Options	....	....
		Input/output	....	....
		Timing/control	....	....
		Operational modes	....	....
	Association	Tasks	....	....
		Devices	....	....
	Implementation	Selection	....	....
		Installation	....	....
		Testing	....	....
		Environment	....	....
		Maintenance	....	....
		Utilities	....	....
	Fail safe/protection	Failure detection	....	....
		Interlocks	....	....
		Trips	....	....
		Recovery procedure	....	....
		Security	....	....
		Verification	....	....
	Failure modes	Not initiated	....	....
		Incorrectly initiated	....	....
		Not terminated	....	....
		Incorrectly terminated	....	....
		Erroneous operation	....	....
		No input/output	....	....
		Incorrect input/output	....	....
		Lockup	....	....
		Too fast	....	....
		Too slow	....	....
		Defective hardware	....	....
		Failure not detected	....	....

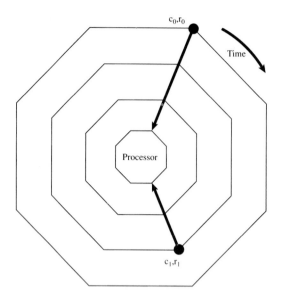

Figure 2.3   Event time diagram showing two tasks.

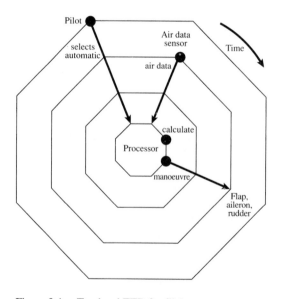

Figure 2.4   Top level ETD for flight management system.

5.4 EVENT TIME DIAGRAM

We propose a new graphical technique, called an event time diagram (ETD) for viewing and decomposing tasks. We find this technique useful for focusing on the safety aspects of the 'total' system. An ETD is used to model events in terms of tasks, time, control and data flow, components and associated functional levels. An ETD may be viewed as a polar diagram where the angle represents time, the distance from the centre gives the functional level, and the arrows give direction of flow of information (either control or data). A node within an ETD may be defined by two co-ordinates (c_x and r_x), where c_x represents the component and r_x represents the functional level (see Figure 2.3).

Referring back to the incident from the avionics industry, the tasks related to the flight management system and collection of air data can be drawn as shown in Figure 2.4.

5.5 SUMMARY OF METHODOLOGY

The task-based hazard identification methodology consists of a number of iterative steps. It makes use of the ETD technique, the task structures and the associated questions for analysing tasks. The whole hazard identification process is outlined in Figure 2.5 on page 64. The step in italic type is optional. A requirement or task is selected for analysis if it is safety-critical. However, a task may also be selected for Chazop in order to find operating problems. When analysing a task, it is not necessary that all the considerations, attributes or questions be used; only the relevant ones need to be examined. Otherwise the Chazop process would be too time-consuming.

6. A CASE STUDY

The case study chosen is based on a rotary screen line printing machine. The development of such a machine requires a multi-disciplinary approach, bringing together expertise in process engineering, logic control, variable speed drives and mechanical engineering. A common problem in assessing the safety of a system is that there is no single discipline uniquely suited to analyse the 'total' system. The application of the methodology to this case study reveals the advantages and disadvantages of the methodology.

The rotary screen printing press consists of a number of print stations (see Figure 2.6 on page 65). Each print station prints a different pattern. Material flow is shown in Figure 2.7 on page 65: paper passes to a print head where it is coated with plastisol (which is a kind of paste); it then passes through a drying cabinet, before passing to the next print station. Three different types of computer system are used. One computer controls the running of the line. Each print

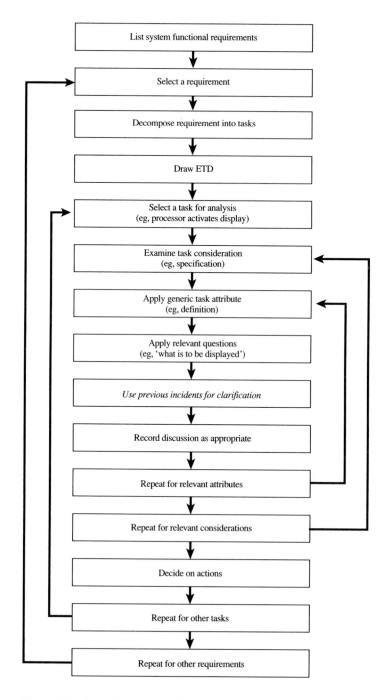

Figure 2.5   Basic Chazop method.

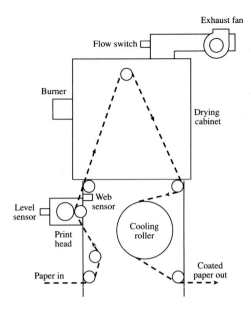

Figure 2.6   Print station.

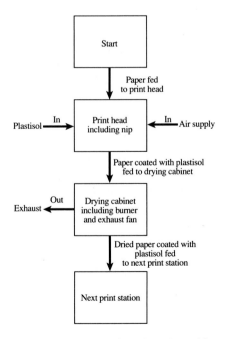

Figure 2.7   Material flow through machine.

head has a single board computer to control the printing. The burner inside each drying cabinet has an associated proportional, integral and derivative temperature controller which adjusts the fuel gas flow to maintain the cabinet at the set temperature.

The use and control of flammable solvents in printing inks and plastisols is a well-known source of hazards in the printing industry. Each drying cabinet in the machine has explosion panels; the machine user is responsible, however, for ensuring that flammable solvent levels in the circulating air and exhaust air associated with each cabinet are safe as defined in the UK Health and Safety Executive guidance[20].

In this case study, an experienced engineer who knows the printing machine well analysed three functional requirements, all of which are related to the solvent concentration in the drying cabinet. The methodology is used to assess safety aspects of solvent concentration associated with the programmable system.

• Requirement 1 — start-up of plant. Before restarting the machine, consider if there may be residual solvent vapour present from previous operations.

• Requirement 2 — pumping plastisol into print head. Consider controlling the coat weight; if the coat weight applied is greater than that specified for the machine, insufficient solvent vapour will be extracted from the cabinet.

• Requirement 3 — exhaust flow monitoring. Consider what happens if there is no flow from the exhaust and so the vapour concentration in the cabinet increases.

In the following subsections the methodology is applied to each functional requirement in turn. Each requirement is decomposed into tasks and each task is described. An ETD is drawn showing the interrelationship between tasks, the timing, the components involved and the associated functional levels, control flow and data flow. Critical tasks are selected for further analysis. For illustrative purposes, for each requirement only the task that is thought to be the most useful in demonstrating the methodology is selected for further analysis. This analysis is performed by applying attributes and associated questions. Only subsets of attributes and questions are selected from a master set. The subsets chosen depend on the particular task. Finally a list of actions is given including comments, warnings and design constraints.

6.1   ANALYSIS OF REQUIREMENT 1

The requirement selected for analysis is the safe start/restart of the machine. One hazard is that there may be solvent vapour in the dryer at start-up.

TASK DECOMPOSITION

The functional requirement can be decomposed into the following tasks:

(1) Processor activates display.
(2) Operator presses start button.
(3) Processor senses no emergency stops pressed.
(4) Processor senses no web break sensors active.
(5) Processor senses air supply OK.
(6) Processor starts exhaust fan to purge dryer.
(7) Processor starts machine.

EVENT TIME DIAGRAM
The ETD is shown in Figure 2.8. Emergency stop buttons are located at the print station so that the operator can stop the machine at any time. Web break sensors are used to detect any break in the material. The air supply is used to open and close nips (the gaps between the printing rollers). The exhaust fan is used to remove solvent vapour from the drying cabinet. The digitally-controlled drives synchronize the passage of material through the print heads.

SELECT TASK FOR ANALYSIS
Task 1, the display task, is very important as it allows the operator to monitor the start-up conditions and to intervene if necessary.

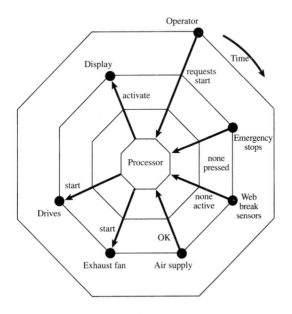

Figure 2.8   ETD for start-up of plant.

TASK CONSIDERATION

Subsets of attributes and questions related to a display task are used.

Specification

Definition: Q: What is to be displayed?

             A: Information about states on the machine.

Objective: Q: Why does information need to be displayed?

             A: To permit the operator to monitor start-up conditions and to allow manual intervention if necessary.

I/O: Q: What are the I/Os for this task?

      A: Status of line (pre-start-up, starting, running, normal shutdown, emergency shutdown), emergency push buttons, web break sensors, air supply.

      Q: What is the format for displaying information?

      A: Icons for identifiers, states in alphanumerics, any unexpected states to flash in red.

Timing/   Q: How often does this information need to be updated.

control: A: Every two seconds.

Action (1)

Operational   Q: What relationship does this task have to normal shutdown?

modes: A: The display is also used in the shutdown sequence to allow the operator to monitor a safe shutdown.

      Q: What relationship does this task have to an emergency shutdown?

      A: The display (in conjunction with an audible alarm) is also used in the emergency shutdown sequence to warn the operator and to permit intervention if necessary.

Action (2)

Implementation

Selection: Q: What type of display will be used?

         A: A VDU.

Installation: Q: If this display is used to show other information, how is information unique to this task distinguished?

         A: The display format is paged; at start-up the default is the start-up page; similarly for normal shutdown and

68

emergency shutdown. At other times, the page is
pre-start-up, normal running or the operator selects the
page with the information requested.

Environment: Q: What particular aspects of the environment may affect the
operation of this task?
A: The environment is 'dirty' and hot close to the printing
head on the machine. The operator must be provided with
the necessary clothing when in this area. The VDU will be
placed in a flame-proof enclosure.

Maintenance: Q: What maintenance procedures are required for this task?
A: A software test module will be used to test the display and
inputs from various sensors. This will also prove useful for
testing operation of the sensors.

Action (3)

Fail safe/protection

Failure   Q: How will failure of the display task be detected?
detection: A: When the display is operating correctly a number in the top
right hand corner of the display will continually update.
Failure of this number to update will indicate the display
task has failed.

Action (4)

Interlocks: Q: What are the preconditions for initiation of any
associated tasks?
A: Start button pressed, no emergency stops pressed,
web break sensors inactive, air supply OK.

Fault recovery Q: What fault recovery procedures are associated with this task?
procedure: A: Where possible any warnings given on the display will
have an associated help page which will give the operator
information on what to do.

Failure modes

Incorrectly Q: How could the task be incorrectly initiated?
initiated: A: If there are no default displays. To prevent this, if there is
power to the VDU, it always shows some display — that is,

69

start-up, normal shutdown, emergency shutdown or if not in any of the previous modes then pre-start-up, running mode or some page selected by the operator.

Actions

(1) Check whether two seconds is appropriate for updating display.

(2) Detail what help will be provided with the warnings on the display as it has to be clear to the operator how to respond to warnings.

(3) Verify that the test routine for checking the display in conjunction with the sensors is useful.

(4) The idea of a number in the top right hand corner of the display needs to be tested. Normally, the number will be continuously updating; however, on the rare occasion that it does not update will this be obvious to the operator?

6.2 ANALYSIS OF REQUIREMENT 2

The requirement is to pump the correct quantity of plastisol into the print head when automatic mode is chosen. A pump at each print station fills the print head at intervals, and the time between intervals is dependent on the required coat weight. If the pump overfills the print head, the solvent concentration in the dryer will increase and may increase beyond the specified limit for the dryer, resulting in a hazard.

TASK DECOMPOSITION

The functional requirement can be decomposed into the following tasks:

(1) Operator selects automatic mode for pump operation.

(2) Line sensor indicates that line is running.

(3) Nip sensor indicates that nip is closed.

(4) Level sensor indicates low plastisol level in print head.

(5) Processor determines pump running time t, based on line speed and required coat weight.

(6) Processor switches the pump on for time t.

EVENT TIME DIAGRAM

Figure 2.9 shows the ETD. The pump can operate in automatic or manual mode. Automatic mode is operative only when the line is running and the nip is closed. The pump is switched on when the level detector detects a low plastisol level in the print head.

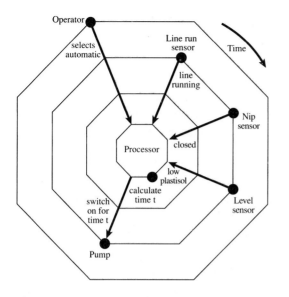

Figure 2.9   ETD for pumping plastisol into print head.

SELECT TASK FOR ANALYSIS

The safety aspect of this requirement ultimately depends on task 6, the switching on of pump for time *t*. It would appear to be the most useful task to analyse for present purposes.

TASK CONSIDERATION

Subsets of attributes and questions related to an actuator task are used.

Specification

Definition: Q: What action is required?

                A: To turn on the pump for a set time.

                                                                Action (1)

Objective: Q: Why is this action required?

                A: To fill the print head with the required amount of plastisol.

Options: Q: What other way could this task be accomplished?

                A: Rather than using the level sensor to trigger switching on pump, a detector which directly measures coat weight could be used.

                                                                Action (2)

I/O:	Q:	What are the I/Os for this task?
	A:	The pump solenoid receives an energize signal from the main system.
	Q:	What is the range of this signal?
	A:	On/off only. No associated range.
	Q:	What parameters are associated with this task?
	A:	'Line speed' and 'pump factor'. 'Pump factor' is set by the operator. It is dependent on the coat weight required.

Timing/   Q: How is this task to be initiated?
control: A: Level probe senses that the plastisol level is low.

Action (3)

Q: How is this task to be terminated?
A: The task is terminated after a time *t* set by the main programmable system which de-energizes the pump solenoid.

Action (4)

Operational   Q: What relationship does this task have to manual mode?
modes: A: In manual mode the pump action is interlocked only to the level sensor; the pump action is independent of line speed and status of nip.

Implementation

Selection: Q: What actuator will be used?
    A: A solenoid valve.

Installation: Q: How will this device be interfaced to the system?
    A: The solenoid valve is energized via a signal from an electromechanical relay. One input of the relay is connected to the programmable system via a digital output.

Testing: Q: How will the implementation be tested?
    A: The switch-on time of the pump is dependent on coat weights. The coat weight is related to the pattern being printed on the paper. Trials are required.
    Q: What reliability data is available on hardware items?
    A: There are no reliability data available at present.

Action (5)

Fail safe/protection

Failure
detection:

Q: How will the system know if any of the hardware
devices associated with this task are functioning
incorrectly/defective?

A: There are no directly associated detection mechanisms as
there is no automated feedback from the coating operation.
Detection is dependent on the operator.

Interlocks:

Q: What are the preconditions for initiation of any
associated tasks?

A: Line running, nip closed, level sensor indicating low
plastisol.

Trips:

Q: What trips are associated with this task?

A: There are no trips associated with this task.

Security:

Q: What parameters associated with this task can be modified
by the operator?

A: The 'pump factor'.

Q: Why can these parameters be modified by the operator?

A: There are many different coat weights required and there
are always inconsistencies within batches.

Failure modes

Lockup:

Q: How could this task lock up?

A: No signal to deactivate the pump so plastisol would overfill
the print head, resulting in excessive coating. To prevent
this, incorporate in the software a maximum on-time for the
pump which, if exceeded, would trip power to the pump.

Action (6)

Actions

(1) In order to be able to select and set up the pump on-time, the operator may
need training.

(2) It would be worth considering the use of an on-line coat weight monitor as
there would be immediate feedback on excessive coating. This would be useful
for safety, from an economic point of view and for better consistency in coating.
The difficulty of using such a device is that the coat weight profile varies across
the paper for a given pattern and there are also variations due to inconsistencies
in batch production (that is, continual recalibration would be required).

(3) Check calibration of level sensor as the operation of the pump is dependent on the sensitivity of the level sensor.

(4) Trials are required to determine maximum and minimum pump on-times.

(5) Obtain hardware reliability data on the pump and associated devices.

(6) Consider installing a trip in case of the pump remaining on unintentionally.

6.3   ANALYSIS OF REQUIREMENT 3

If no solvent vapour is being exhausted from the drying cabinet while the line is running, the machine must be shut down and placed in a safe state.

TASK DECOMPOSITION

The functional requirement can be decomposed into the following tasks:

(1) Flow switch indicates no exhaust flow.

(2) Line sensor indicates line is running.

(3) Processor switches off burners.

(4) Processor opens nip.

(5) Processor keeps line running.

(6) Processor activates alarm.

(7) Processor shows warning on display.

EVENT TIME DIAGRAM

Figure 2.10 shows the ETD. The burner is switched off to remove the heat source from the drying cabinet. The nip is forced open to stop coating the paper and the line is kept running to remove the paper from the oven and prevent it from igniting. The siren is activated and a warning is displayed.

SELECT TASK FOR ANALYSIS

Task 1, the operation of the flow switch, is critical. Incorrect operation or logic associated with this device could lead to catastrophic events.

TASK CONSIDERATION

Subsets of attributes and questions related to a sensor task are used.

Specification

Definition: Q: What state is to be monitored?

A: The exhaust flow.

Objective: Q: Why does this state need to be monitored?

A: To prevent build-up of solvent concentration in the drying cabinet.

Options: Q: What other way could this task be accomplished?
                A: A single sensor which directly measures solvent concentration or one which measures air flow.

Actions (1), (2)

I/O: Q: What are the I/Os for this task?
                A: Output signal from the flow switch indicating no exhaust flow.
                Q: Over what range is the signal to be monitored?
                A: Output signal on/off, no associated range.

Timing/   Q: How often does this state have to be scanned?
control: A: The scan time should be less than a second.

Operational   Q: What relationship does this task have to start-up?
modes: A: The flow switch is associated with a purge sequence which must complete before start-up.

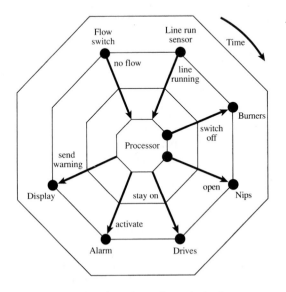

Figure 2.10   ETD for exhaust flow monitoring.

Implementation

Selection: Q: What sensor will be used?

A: An air flow failure detector which has an embedded mercury switch.

Installation: Q: How will this device be interfaced to the system?

A: The mercury switch is connected to a electromechanical relay. One output of the relay is connected to the programmable system via a digital input.

Q: How will this device be calibrated?

A: The device is supplied by the manufacturer calibrated; it will be tested when the machine is being commissioned.

Action (3)

Q: Where will this device be positioned?

A: In the exhaust ducting, not near any disturbances — for example, fresh air dampers.

Testing: Q: What reliability data is available on hardware items?

A: There is no reliability data available on the flow switch.

Action (4)

Environment: Q: What particular aspects of the environment may affect the operation of this task?

A: The environment is hot and laden with plastisol fumes. The device works on the principle of difference in pressure inside and outside the exhaust duct. Clean air outside the duct activates the device.

Maintenance: Q: What maintenance procedures are required for this task?

A: The condition and operation of the switch should be checked by hand regularly because of its importance and the corrosive environment in which it is placed.

Action (5)

Fail safe/protection

Failure detection: Q: What alarms are associated with this task?

A: A siren and alarm message on a display.

Action (6)

Q: What is the purpose of these alarms?

A: To warn the operator that the sensor has indicated no flow in the exhaust, and to check that the machine is shut down safely.

Q: How will the system know if the sensor is performing OK?

A: There will be a test sequence pre-start-up which will check the sensor indicates 'off' state with the exhaust fan off indicating no exhaust flow and 'on' state with the fan on to indicate there is an exhaust flow.

Interlocks: Q: What are the preconditions for initiation of any associated tasks?

A: The flow sensor indicates no flow and the line sensor indicates line running.

Q: How are conditions of completion of any associated tasks checked?

A: They must be checked manually by the operator.

Trips: Q: What trips are associated with this task?

A: The nip is forced off and the burner is switched off.

Q: Why are these trips required?

A: The nip is opened to stop coating; the burner is switched off to remove the heat source.

Fault recovery Q: What fault recovery procedures are associated with this task?
procedure: A: Manually test operation of the exhaust fan and sensor, purge the dryer and measure the concentration of the solvent in the dryer.

Failure modes

Incorrectly Q: How could the task be incorrectly terminated?
terminated: A: If the operator presses the emergency stop, this would leave coated material in the dryer which may ignite. To prevent this, the siren should be unique to this task, indicating that no operator intervention is required.

Too slow: Q: How could task response be too slow?

A: If the response of the sensor was too slow, this would cause a build-up of solvent vapour in the dryer and possible subsequent explosion.

Action (7)

Actions

(1) The dependence on a single device for monitoring exhaust flow is questionable.

(2) It is worth considering on-stream solvent monitoring rather than an air flow switch. First, it measures the required parameter directly and, second, continuous feedback from on-stream monitoring could detect a unpredicted rise in solvent concentration. The major disadvantages of this are cost and number required.

(3) Correct calibration is essential.

(4) Hardware reliability information is required to make sure the device is robust enough for the number of operations and the environment.

(5) A good maintenance procedure for the device is essential, because of its importance and the 'dirty' environment. The device should be easily accessible for the same reasons.

(6) The alarm siren should be readily identifiable as being associated with a 'dangerous' level of solvent vapour.

(7) Verify the response time of the sensor is adequate.

7.   SUMMARY AND DISCUSSION

Safety assessment is an important activity in the design and development of safety-critical systems. This chapter has focused on the hazard identification aspect of safety assessment. Although much research work has been done on developing Chazop, there is no agreed format on how it should be done at the moment. The development approaches that have been taken so far are *ad hoc*. However, a consensus that emerges from the four different Chazop schemes described briefly in this chapter is that Chazop requires a 'total' system view. When assessing a system the hardware, software and their interactions all need to be considered.

We have described a systematic approach for developing a hazard identification methodology. The methodology is based on analysis of past incidents. The results of the analysis form the basis of the methodology. The key elements of the methodology include questions derived from past incidents, task structures which group the questions in a logical way, and a new graphical technique (ETD) for decomposing and viewing tasks. The methodology is used to assess a system by considering each requirement in turn using the following basic steps:

(1) Decompose requirement into tasks.

(2) Draw ETD showing tasks.

(3) Identify critical tasks.

(4) For critical tasks, apply associated questions.

We have shown how application of the methodology has provided a means of systematically assessing the safety aspects of controlling solvent vapour on a printing machine. The development of such a machine requires expertise in many disciplines. However, the application of the methodology is relatively simple.

Once we have identified that flammable solvent is a source of hazards, this fact is used to guide selection of tasks for analysis. Not all the task attributes/guide words or associated questions were applied to the selected tasks. The subset of attributes and questions applied to any one task depends on how effective particular attributes or questions are in assessing the safety aspects related to that task. The drawing of an ETD provides a useful way of establishing, understanding and analysing the tasks involved in any one requirement. The I/O functional level of the ETDs has received the most attention in this application, as it is a control application and the methodology is being used at the design requirements stage. The emphasis would shift to the control and processing level of the ETDs at the detailed design stage.

The application of the methodology complements the design of a programmable system. It not only assesses safety but improves the overall quality of the system.

As would be expected in any systematic safety assessment, application of the methodology is time-consuming. A computer support tool would prove very useful and provide a documented record for any company. This record would prove useful for future designs or re-engineering old designs. It would also be beneficial in the event of an incident. We are developing a software support tool based on the methodology.

REFERENCES IN CHAPTER 2

1. International Electrotechnical Commission, 1995, *Draft IEC 1508 — Functional Safety: Safety-Related Systems, Parts 1 to 6* (IEC Sub-committee 65A).

2. Institution of Electrical Engineers, 1992, *Safety-Related Systems — A Professional Brief for the Engineer* (IEE, London).

3. Health and Safety Executive, 1987, *Programmable Electronic Systems in Safety Related Applications* (Her Majesty's Stationery Office, London).

4. Engineering Equipment and Materials Users Association, 1989, *Safety Related Instrument Systems for the Process Industries*, Publication No. 160 (EEMUA, London).

5.   Institution of Gas Engineers, 1994, *Programmable Equipment in Safety-Related Applications (Safety Recommendations IGE/SR/15)* (IGE, London).
6.   Ministry of Defence, 1993, *Draft Defence Standard 00–56 (Parts 1 and 2): Safety Management Requirements for Defence Systems Containing Programmable Electronics* (MOD, Directorate of Standardization, Glasgow, UK).
7.   Minstry of Defence, 1995, *Draft Interim Defence Standard 00–58: A Guideline for HAZOP Studies on Systems Which Include a Programmable Electronic System* (MOD, Directorate of Standardization, Glasgow, UK).
8.   Lawley, H.G., 1974, *Chemical Engineering Progress*, 70 (4): 45.
9.   Kletz, T.A., 1992, *Hazop and Hazan — Identifying and Assessing Process Industry Hazards*, 3rd edition (Institution of Chemical Engineers, Rugby, UK).
10. Broomfield, E.J. and Chung, P.W.H., 1994, *Applied Computing Review*, 2 (1): 7.
11. McDermid, J.A., 1991, *Reliability Engineering and System Safety*, 32 (1): 1.
12. Duxbury, H.A. and Turney, R.D., 1989, Techniques for the analysis and assessment of hazards in the process industries, paper presented at *New Mexico Technical Research Center for Energetic Materials Open Seminars on Safety and Hazards Evaluation, 11 April 1989.*
13. Modarres, M., 1993, *What Every Engineer Should Know About Reliability and Risk Analysis* (Marcel Dekker, New York).
14. Burns, D.J. and Pitblado, R.M., 1993, A modified HAZOP methodology for safety critical system assessment, in *Directions in Safety-Critical Systems: Proceedings of the Safety-Critical Systems Symposium, Bristol* (edited by Redmill, F. and Anderson, T.) (Springer-Verlag, London).
15. Fink, R., Oppert, S., Collinson, P., Cooke, G., Dhanjal, S., Lesan, H. and Shaw, R., 1993, Data management in clinical laboratory information systems, in *Directions in Safety-Critical Systems: Proceedings of the Safety-Critical Systems Symposium, Bristol* (edited by Redmill, F. and Anderson, T.) (Springer-Verlag, London).
16. Andow, P., 1991, *Guidance on HAZOP Procedures for Computer-Controlled Plants* (Her Majesty's Stationery Office, London).
17. Lear, J.B., 1993, Computer hazard and operability studies, *Sydney University Chemical Engineering Association Symposium: Safety and Reliability of Process Control Systems, October 1993.*
18. Nimmo, I., Nunns, S.R. and Eddershaw, B.W., 1993, *Loss Prevention Bulletin*, 111: 13.
19. Nimmo, I., *Chemical Engineering Progress*, 90 (10): 32.
20. Health and Safety Executive, 1981, *Evaporating and Other Ovens* (Her Majesty's Stationery Office, London).

3. THE REASONS WHY COMPUTER-CONTROLLED SYSTEMS FAIL

Chaim Shen-Orr

'It's all the computer's fault.'
Cashier at a US department store, when a 15% overcharge was discovered

'The software and the accompanying written materials (including instructions for use) are provided 'as is' without warranty of any kind. Further, Microsoft does not warrant, guarantee or make any representations regarding the use, or the results of use, of the software or the written materials in terms of correctness, accuracy, reliability, currentness, or otherwise. The entire risk as to the results and performance of the software is assumed by you.'
A typical software licence agreement

1. INTRODUCTION

Computers are becoming pervasive — there are now computer chips in almost any product imaginable, from Automobiles to Zebra toys, including toasters, rice cookers and chemical plant controllers. As their use spreads in width, depth and importance, they become essential to the proper functioning of society. As a by-product, the implications of computer malfunctions loom larger too.

Computer failures by themselves do not impose any risk to life, limb or property (unless a computer box falls on your foot). It is the *system* aspects of computers — their incorporation into larger systems that control processes directly or advise people what to do — that raise safety concerns. In particular, the safety aspects of software are becoming an issue and attracting research. Reference 1 is a definitive survey, and Reference 2 is highly recommended as a good overview.

In the following sections I describe several reasons for failures in computerized systems, illustrating each with an example. Most of the examples did not cause an actual safety problem, simply because they occurred within systems that are not safety-related. It is fairly easy to visualize, however, what would have happened if they were. Some of these examples appear (sometimes hidden!) in the literature. Others are from my personal experience, or from private communications. An anecdotal list of occurrences is compiled periodically by P.G. Neumann in the 'RISKS' section of *Software Engineering Notes*[3].

2. THE POWER AND THE GLORY

The introduction of computers (or, to be exact, stored program digital computers) revolutionized many industries. Process plants have been able to achieve higher yields at lower costs by replacing 'simple' electromechanical controls with more sophisticated computer controls. These controls execute complex algorithms that optimize the process variables, often using advanced process models based on information obtained through measurements of a host of other process variables.

Such exact and efficient controls have not been possible — or would have been prohibitively expensive — without digital computers. The price of computer hardware has gone down as its performance has gone up over recent years, both by several orders of magnitude. Computer power is measured in 'operations per seconds', and each individual operation is executed in a sequence dictated by programs (or 'software'). A typical current figure for computer power of inexpensive IBM PC-compatibles is around 30 million operations per second, and this figure doubles in about a year and a half.

It is the programs executed by these computers that give them their power, imitating human thoughts with greater precision and speed. Programs are the spirit which brings hunks of metal and silicon into life, makes inert boxes act as intelligent beings, and creates worlds of wonder where nothing had been before. The programmer, just like an ancient magician, builds castles in the air, commanding the inanimate hardware to do his bidding with a typed incantation or a magical touch of a mouse button. 'Few media of creation are so flexible, so easy to polish and rework, so readily capable of realizing grand conceptual structures'[4].

3.   THE DANGERS LURKING

The danger from such usage of computers lies in the very fact that their power is so great, and that in order to realize that power, hardware/software systems of incredible complexity must be built. The more powerful, the more dangerous they are if they fail. And the more complex, the harder it is to avoid failures altogether. Computer failures may be divided into several species:

3.1   HARDWARE FAILURES

Hardware failures in computers are just like failures in any other piece of equipment. They occur randomly, as a result of a defective component, bad design, unexpected environmental conditions, bad maintenance and so on. These failures are random in the sense that several identical units, subjected to the identical circumstances, would each fail (or not fail) at a different time.

Since computer hardware failures are very similar to other electronic equipment failures, I will not dwell on them further, unless they combine with other problems. Some incidents caused by hardware failures are discussed in Chapter 1, Section 2, page 5.

3.2   SOFTWARE FAILURES

Software failures are different in the sense that they are not random. Any number of identical computers whose identical software is subjected to identical inputs will fail at exactly the same point.

One reason for the uniqueness of software is that, in a sense, a computer program is not a physical entity. Rather, it is an embodiment of a logical process. Hence, it cannot wear out, is not affected by heat, rain or vibrations, and — just like the magician's incantation — will do the unexpected if even a single magic word is misspelled (see Chapter 1, item 6.7, page 32).

3.3   SPECIFICATIONS FAILURES

Specifications failures are distinguished by their origins: a defect in the system's specifications, rather than in the design or execution of either hardware or software.

3.4   HUMAN ERRORS

Human errors are caused by an inappropriate action — or lack of action — by a human agent involved in the process. As we shall see, some characteristics of computer-controlled systems tend to induce human errors.

Please note that the 'human agent' referred to here is the system operator. Don't forget that at the root of almost every failure described here are other human beings — namely, the system's specifiers, designers and builders. Their error is not anticipating the circumstances under which a failure could occur!

3.5   MALICIOUS FAILURES

Malicious failures are caused by a relatively new phenomenon, the malicious introduction of programs intended to cause damage to an anonymous user. These programs are popularly known as 'computer viruses'.

4.   COMPLEXITY

One of the advantages of using a computer peripheral known as a 'fax-modem' is that overseas facsimile transmissions (faxes) can be easily scheduled to take place late at night, when phone rates are lowest. A frugal user is likely to set the computer's fax program for a post-midnight transmission, and go to bed.

One of the more popular fax programs at the time of writing is WinFax Pro 3.0, from Delrina Technology Inc. It operates within the Microsoft Windows 3.1 environment, and acts as a printer: to send a fax, the user merely 'prints' to a virtual printer created by WinFax. When that happens the WinFax program loads into memory, and displays a 'Phone Book' from which the recipient and the time of transmission are selected. At the designated time the program activates the fax-modem, and sends the fax to the phone number listed in the 'Phone Book' for the recipient. The program has been on the market for quite a while, and has been a reliable performer. It is marketed worldwide.

The Microsoft Windows operating environment sold in Israel where I live is 'Windows 3.1 with Hebrew Language Support'. It is designed to accommodate applications written specifically for the Hebrew language (word processors, etc), and also 'regular' (English language) applications such as WinFax. You can enter Hebrew text into English applications, but some formatting operations (word wrap, etc) may not come out right.

Late in 1993, Microsoft came out with an improved version of Windows 3.1 with Hebrew Language Support. With that version, if a recipient's name in a WinFax Phone Book entry includes Hebrew characters, the program 'freezes' once a proper fax connection to that recipient is established. The PC sticks, and the fax-modem gets stuck too; the phone connection goes on, but no data are sent.

Now it could very well happen that an Israeli WinFax user would have a good night's sleep, while his modem is busy transmitting sweet nothings the whole night to his uncle in Sydney, Australia. All you need is a Biblical name (easier to write in Hebrew) and a fax machine on the other side that does not disconnect automatically. I don't know of anyone to whom this has actually

happened on an overseas call — it happened to me on in-country long-distance — but certainly all the elements of a financial disaster are there.

The average 'real' computer program is a very complex artifact. The logical structures required for either the program or its underlying operating system are much more complex then any of the previous generation of plant control systems. With systems that complex, it is very difficult — nay, impossible — for a human being to understand and remember all the implications of a slight change during development or maintenance.

We usually think of the software as 'the program', but actually modern software consists of multiple layers. Behind the program lies a compiler or an assembler (the software that translates a high-level or low-level source program into operating machine code), libraries (containing support programs), operating system software, and the BIOS (basic input/output system — the software part of the hardware). The hardware includes the computer itself, and its input/output (I/O) modules, which quite often contain their own computers. For example, each IBM PC's keyboard contains a dedicated computer, programmed to scan the key switches at a high rate. It decodes the key-press combinations, and informs the main computer which keys are pressed using a series of codes transmitted over a pair of wires. And, sure enough, I have seen a system failure caused by a mismatch between the two computers, the PC's and the keyboard's.

Note that even what we usually call 'hardware' may actually include software — 'microcode' built into modern CPUs (central processor units) to translate the programmer's 'machine code' into basic internal register and bus operations. Recently a major news item unfolded concerning an error in Intel's Pentium microcode. The error causes a reduction in accuracy in floating-point divide operations for some bit patterns in the division operands (see Section 7)[5]. Intel's stock dipped approximately 12% following announcement of the error over the Internet, forcing the company to offer free replacement for approximately six million Pentium chips.

5.　　INTEGRITY

An automatic teller machine (ATM) at a bank branch office had a hardware failure in late 1979, resulting in the year reading as '00' instead of '79'. The unit was repaired in a week.

ATMs are designed to prevent card thieves withdrawing large sums of money by going from one machine to another and withdrawing the maximum amount that each allows. They do this by setting a limit to the total amount withdrawn per day, regardless of the number of withdrawals and the number of ATMs involved. For this end, the machines read and write two data items on the cards' magnetic strip — the date used and the total amount of money withdrawn through the card per day. Thus, for one week at one machine, the withdrawal date was incorrectly written on each card and on each transaction receipt.

That does not seem like a serious problem, and probably was not. The *real* problem was that the date algorithm used by the ATM's computers at all bank branch offices at the time used the equivalent of two decimal digits for the year, thus interpreting '00' as the year 2000.

Part of the computer program used in all ATMs at the time is shown in 'pseudo-code' in Table 3.1. Notice that in the third statement ('if <last withdrawal date> is earlier than <today's date> ...) the programmer made the implicit assumption that the date read in from the card is either earlier than today's, or today's. This is a perfectly reasonable assumption, since there are no time machines around to bring to the present cards which have been used in the future. The hardware problem, however, effectively created such a 'time machine' — and the algorithm just described created a situation where the data on the card was 'stuck in the year 2000'!

TABLE 3.1
ATM program segment pseudo-code

Read 'amount requested' from keyboard and store it in variable <amount requested>.
Read data for variables <last withdrawal date> and <prior total withdrawal> from
    'last withdrawal date' and 'prior total withdrawal' on the card's magnetic strip.

If <last withdrawal date> is earlier than <today's date>, then:
    Set <last withdrawal date> to <today's date>,
    Set <prior total withdrawal> to zero.

Set <current maximum> to (<daily maximum> − <prior total withdrawal>).
If <current maximum> is equal to or smaller than zero, then:
    Display 'Sorry, Card Overdrawn'
    Go to Exit.

Set <authorized withdrawal> to (the smaller of <amount requested> and
    <current maximum>).
Use information about available bank notes to figure <money to be dispensed>
    (equal to or smaller than <authorized withdrawal>).
Dispense money equal to <money to be dispensed>.

If money dispensing completed successfully then:
    Write (<money to be dispensed> + <prior total withdrawal>) to 'prior total
        withdrawal' on the card's magnetic strip,
    Write <last withdrawal date> to 'last withdrawal date' on the card's magnetic
        strip,
    Go to Exit.

If money dispensing not completed ...
:
:

Exit: Print receipt
Eject card
:
:

The following notation is used in this 'pseudo-code' section:
- indented text is executed if previous condition is satisfied;
- <xxx> — a variable used in the program;
- 'yyy' — an input or output (from/to ATM keyboard, magnetic card, or display);
- (zzz) — used as in arithmetic or English.

All the customers who had used their cards even once at that particular ATM during that week, started to accumulate 'money withdrawn' on their card's magnetic strip. In time, each of them would run up to the limit, and could not use ATMs anywhere in the country. The bank had to apologize, and to set a special program to reset 'stuck' cards.

A computer-controlled system is not just its hardware or its software, it is a combination of the two. And, as in many other cases, the combination is greater than the sum of the parts, especially with regards to failure modes. In other words, the software has to be designed considering hardware failure modes, and vice versa. This is easier said than done, especially when the complexity of both hardware and software is considered. In addition, quite often the programmers are not plant people, and are unfamiliar with the facts of life on the factory floor.

6.   INABILITY TO TEST COMPLETELY

A US Army Raytheon Patriot missile battery defending the air base at Dhahran, Saudi Arabia, failed to detect, engage and intercept an incoming Iraqi Scud missile on the night of 25 February 1991. The missile hit an Army barracks, killing 28 US soldiers. The cause of the failure, according to the US Army, was, 'The battery had been up and running for a long time using what is known as the version 34 software ... [the cause of the failure was] a timing error associated with the version 34 software'[6].

There are several 'clocks' within the missile battery fire control computer, mostly implemented in software by accumulation — that is, adding, several times a second, small increments (fractions of a second) to a memory cell. Due to the finite length of the digital word used in a computer, the representation of fractions is inaccurate unless the fractions are a power of two (such as 1/8). The 'round-off' error in each operation is very small — typically 10^{-7} — but it accumulates over a large number of such additions. Slightly different methods of handling accumulations, which look as though they ought to have the same result, produce different round-off errors. The problem in the Patriot fire control software was that not all the clocks used exactly the same method, so the timing difference between the clocks would grow with time.

Usually, a missile battery is 'brought down' every so often, either for maintenance or when the military exercise is over. As a side-effect, the accumulated round-off error is reset to zero. Thus, the problem was not encountered during system tests in the laboratory or at White Sands Missile Range.

Dhahran was no test range, and under the pressure to defend against Scuds coming in every so often, the battery was not brought down. The mismatch in time value between two system clocks was therefore allowed to grow until it was large enough to cause a synchronization problem and prevent the system from recognizing an incoming target[7].

In a sense, a software failure is different from a hardware failure: software never wears out, no matter what the environmental conditions or the external stresses may be. It is more like a set trap: whenever the right combination of data sequences comes along, it will always fail in exactly the same manner. So, the question is, why was the failure not found during testing? In principle, a well-designed test program like the one conducted by the US Army for the Patriot missile system should provide complete testing. This includes 'off-nominal' combinations of conditions that may occur due to failures of auxiliary control equipment (sensors, actuators, interfaces and human operators).

Complete system testing implies that every reachable logical state the system can go through has been exercised. Computer programs are often documented using 'flow charts' in which the computational processes are depicted as arrows (with accompanying text describing the computation to be carried out), and decision processes are depicted as 'decision boxes'. A decision, based on values resulting from previous computations or external inputs, determines which process to carry out next. The origins of all data values are either external data read in through sensors, or input by human operators, or constants included as a part of a program. Figure 3.1[8] describes a fairly simple program. Any 'path' through the program may be the one that triggers a failure — for example, going twice through the upper part of the first loop, followed by going ten times through the lower, followed by five times through a 'zigzag' through the second loop.

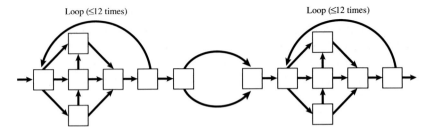

Figure 3.1   A flow chart for a fairly simple computer program. Arrows represent computations and boxes represent decisions on which path to follow next. The number of possible paths could be as high as 10^{19} so it is impossible to test them all (after Boehm[8]).

A quick calculation shows that the number of such distinct paths through this simple program exceeds 10^{19}. On a fast computer that can execute the whole program in a millisecond, a thorough test traversing every path will take approximately 3×10^8 years, certainly not a practical proposition. So, any 'non-trivial' (that is, 'practical') program cannot be completely tested.

Two additional points:

- not all decision points are evident in a flow chart. Division by zero, for example, results in an 'error interrupt' that takes the program out of its normal flow. Thus, there should be additional 'decision boxes' following each basic operation in the normal flow chart, each box catering for one of the machine-generated error conditions that may be triggered by that operation. Section 9 mentions one such error interrupt (see page 94);
- the flow chart assumes that the hardware and underlying software are operating correctly. This assumption is not necessarily true.

7.   UNLIMITED PROPAGATION SPACE

Multics, an early large-scale multi-user operating system developed at MIT, was having infrequent mysterious 'crashes' (total breakdowns). Usually, 'system crashes' occur at peak activity periods, when the system's resources are straining to meet demand. These crashes, however, would occur at off-peak hours — hence the mystery. After a while, somebody noticed a pattern and the solution was quick. It turned out that around midnight in months with 31 days, the memory location assigned to the system 'Time&Date' overflowed*. An unrelated system program was using the adjacent bits affected by the overflow, and with its data corrupted, it would bring down the system when it ran some time after such a midnight.

When dealing with physical processes — be they mechanical, flow, or electric — we can visualize the 'flow' of process elements from one station to the next. Thus, a failure at one location will propagate to a physically-adjacent location via appropriate physical connections — contacts, pipes, conduits, leakage paths, 'sneak paths' and so on. Each particular failure mode propagates through a limited number of system paths, to reach a limited subset of the system's physical devices. I will term this phenomenon 'limited propagation space'.

---

*   An overflow is an error condition in which a result is too large to fit into its intended cell — for example, when a division by a very small number produces a very large number.

Modern computers are examples of 'Von Neumann machines', in which the same memory contains both data and programs. In a sense, programs *are* data. For example, the input data to a compiler is a program source (the bit patterns in memory corresponding to the program text). Thus, program instructions and data look alike: words composed of binary 'bits' each have a value of either '0' or '1'. A typical instruction is composed of an *opcode* (operation code) portion telling the control processor unit what to do, and an *operand* portion telling it what to do it on. Usually, the operand is specified as an *address* in memory, or as integer data. For example, the IBM 360 basic opcode for 'fixed-point full-word divide' is 01011101. Changing just one bit, 11011101 is 'logical translate and test'. The same bit patterns also mean address (or integer data) '93' and '221', respectively.

A software error may cause an instruction word to be regarded as data or address, and vice versa. Overwriting even one bit in the opcode portion of an instruction causes a completely different operation to be carried out on completely different data. A change of even one bit in the address portion of a 'store' instruction causes it to store a bit pattern in a wrong location, anywhere in memory. That bit pattern may corrupt an instruction or a piece of data used by another, totally unrelated, part of the program. When that part executes, more errors are created, and so on. There are no physical limits — proximity, time, etc — to the 'distance' between the location where the original error occurs and the affected location. An error can reach all of the 'universe' available to the software, and can stay there, waiting for the failure to occur, 'for eternity'. Thus, the error has an 'unlimited propagation space'.

Since unlimited propagation spaces do not occur in nature, the human mind is not 'tuned' to deal with problems that may be described in these terms. Thus, errors leading to that kind of problem are very difficult to prevent. Modern computer languages and operating systems do help, by allocating resources automatically and separating program elements. Still, bugs (the nickname for software errors) in these facilities themselves may cause even more complicated errors ... .

8. ERROR SENSITIVITY

The transfer function of an old-style electronic servo controller is typically determined by ±1% resistors and ±5% capacitors. When the controller is replaced by a digital computer, what is the 'tolerance' of the program code?

Most process control computer programs make use of data table interpolation. A typical one-dimensional data table contains two sets of numbers: an 'argument table' and a corresponding 'function table', with the same number of entries. A typical interpolation subroutine first performs 'table lookup', traversing the argument table until it locates the entries straddling the current input value. It then interpolates between the corresponding function table entries to obtain an output value.

A rather spectacular crash of a test missile was caused by a simple typographical error in a data table for a relatively unimportant function. The typo placed a minus sign in front of a number in the argument table.

The input value was unlikely to come close to the erroneous table entry, so the interpolation subroutine was never exercised over that portion of the table during software testing. In actual flight the physical value of the input never came close to the erroneous entry either, but a combination of three different unplanned-for factors caused the *computed* input value to exceed it. Had it been an analogue system, nothing serious would have happened; in that flight regime, flight control would not have been jeopardized by even a ±30% inaccuracy in the function output value.

Argument tables are conventionally arranged in ascending numerical order, and the table lookup algorithm assumed it was so. The real effect of the typo was not in changing the value of a table entry, but in violating that assumption. Encountering a situation in which the next table entry was smaller then the last, the table lookup routine went into an infinite loop.

The computer system contained a watchdog (see item 13.1.1, page 103), which stopped the loop in a little while and started a back-up program for the rest of the current control loop cycle. Unfortunately, the basic problem remained, causing the watchdog to trigger again and again. Worse, the location from which the errant routine was called was such that the back-up program received some essential data dating back to the last valid cycle. Since there was no new valid data coming up, loss of control was inevitable.

Note that the error itself was insignificant. Had it been in the function table, or a change in value that did not cause a reversal of order, nothing would have happened. But, in general, there is no such thing as a 'small' error in a computer program: any error can bring down the whole house, in a manner that does not necessarily have anything to do with the intended purpose of the code in which the error appears. In other words, the allowed 'tolerance' in computer code is essentially zero.

9.   COMPATIBILITY

The field of computers is a fast-moving one, with new and better hardware and software appearing daily. Progress is so fast that a computer may be obsolete in two years, and the basic components required for its maintenance may not be available after five years. A computer architecture may be obsolete in ten years. 'Invisible' components such as operating systems and compilers, used to generate machine code from higher-order languages such as Fortran or C, are also updated frequently.

The only way such a dynamic industry can survive is on the basis of '100% downward compatibility'; in other words, each new model is supposed to do what the previous one did in exactly the same manner. Sometimes compatibility is designed into the hardware, and sometimes it is obtained by 'emulation' — an extra layer of software that makes a new (and sometimes radically different) system appear to older programs as if they were running in a familiar system.

Both downward compatibility and emulation enable the industry to keep a fast pace while maintaining users' investment in software, data and

trained personnel. In most cases the user gains speed right away, and additional capabilities are utilized when new software comes along.

Even users who do not seek progress are affected. As time goes by spare parts get scarce, and support for older software versions deteriorates. Existing computers have to be replaced by newer models, and software changes (perhaps due to plant or process modification) have to be compiled using newer versions of the language compilers. Users assume that both hardware and software are '100% compatible' but in practice subtle differences sometimes do exist between successive versions of '100%-compatible' hardware and software. Some differences are intentional and some unintentional.

For example, the Intel 80286 CPU used in IBM PC AT-class computers is downward compatible with the Intel 8086/8088 CPUs used in XT-class PCs. This is so, *except* that the address pushed to the 'stack' on detection of a divide overflow (see page 90) is different*. The address of the 'interrupted' instruction is pushed onto the stack in one case, the one following it in the other[9]. The newer model is 'better' — the result is more useful — but it is also *different*. Thus, a program that uses the older features may not operate correctly once that old XT, no longer serviceable, is replaced by a newer AT.

Every so often during my doctoral research, I had to produce a plot from a set of data points on punched cards. Each set had to be pre-processed by multiplying its X values by a constant. One day I noticed that the parameter list for the laboratory's drum plotter had an option for two separate scale factors, one for the X axis and one for the Y axis. Being lazy, I figured I could use this feature to save the pre-processing operation: set the Y scale factor to fit the paper, and set the X factor to a value calculated from the constant and the Y factor.

Drum plotter paper comes in continuous rolls, rather than in fixed-size sheets. This helps running a 'batch shop', since the operator does not have to change paper after each plot. The length of each plot is determined by the software, without anybody having to actually change paper. In my case, the length of the plot was supposed to be about 12 inches.

What came out instead was a sheet of expensive plot paper several hundred feet long, with just one line running at the bottom along the whole length. A thorough examination showed this line to be the bottom serif of the

---

*   A 'stack' is an arrangement for temporary storage of data, in which computer words are pushed on or pulled off as needed. The CPU uses a stack to store information on how to proceed when returning from an interruption of the normal program flow.

left leg of the letter 'M', the first letter of a logo drawn at the corner of the paper, just prior to plotting the data. The cause was quickly found to be the use of non-identical X and Y scaling, which apparently nobody had used for some years.

Now how come? Starting to investigate, I was told that the software drivers for the drum plotter were written and fully debugged in the laboratory, a long time ago. I was using an IBM 370, but before that the laboratory had an IBM 360, with which the 370 was downward compatible. Before the 360 they had an IBM 7090, and to save programming effort at the time the computer was changed, the plotter driver code was not rewritten. Instead, an emulation program was used to run the 7090's code on the 360. Digging deeper, I was told that the original code may have been written for either the earlier IBM 704, or the IBM 650 that the laboratory had earlier still[10]. At each change-of-generation the plotter driver software went through another layer of emulation, or relied on compatibility. The plotter itself was also changed several times, each time relying either on compatibility or on emulation.

At this stage I concluded that the work involved in finding where the error came from would probably earn me a doctoral degree in history (where do you find programming manuals for an IBM 704?). I was not seeking such a degree at the time, and the investigation was abandoned.

As far as I know, the systems group solved this bug later by inserting an extra layer of software that prevented use of different X and Y scale factors, rather then by rewriting the code. And, some time later, the old 370 was replaced by a software-compatible Amdahl V5.

Talking about compatibility, what do we have to be compatible with? An example of the issues involved is illustrated by the '40-tracks' story. A 'floppy disk' (or diskette) drive is a member of a family classified by IBM as DASD, which stands for 'direct access storage device'. This means that the sys-

tem can reach a piece of information stored on the diskette without 'fast forwarding' or 'rewinding' to it. Information is written on the diskette in concentric rings ('tracks'), which are reached by moving a read/write heads assembly over a rotating magnetic-media diskette. The information stored in each track is accessed as the diskette rotates under the heads.

The original IBM PC 360-KB diskette drive was specified to have 40 tracks and indeed its disk operating system (DOS) enabled diskette operations between tracks zero to 39 only. The mechanical design of the drive mechanism was such that it could reach further, and clever programmers were able to by-pass DOS and make use of the extra space in track 40. One typical use was for 'copy protection' schemes, since ordinary users were prevented by DOS from accessing and copying that extra information.

Some later drives did have a hard stop at track 39. The resulting outcry from owners of 'track 40' software forced the manufacturers to go back to the old-style drives without the hard stop. So, the 'compatibility standard' was not the published specification, but rather the *de facto* standard established by the actual hardware that arrived first on the market.

10.   HUMAN INTERACTIONS

Human operators interact with computers in several ways. They enter data, control action, monitor activity and respond to alarms.

People performed these tasks a long time before the digital computer was invented, but the combination of man and computer proved highly effective. The result is an unparalleled growth in breadth and depth of application of computers, both in industry and in daily life. As computer usage grows, new problems and sensitivities are revealed along with the benefits, and unfortunately some of these problems have to do with safety. Not all these problems are due to inherent features of computers; some are caused by shifts in design convenience, and some are due to lack of appreciation of human factors issues.

Consider data entry and readout. In the olden days, people used to adjust a knob or a slider, while watching a pointer or a dial. Now they usually watch and type in numbers, the old 'analogue' being replaced by the new 'digital'. In fact it could have been done 'digitally' before; it was more expensive, but sometimes it was done. It can still be done now in an 'analogue' fashion — graphically — and sometimes that is done too. Indeed, with the proliferation of graphical user interface (GUI) operating systems, long columns of numbers may be out of fashion again!.

Still, in the main, computer data are entered and read as a list of characters or digits; it is easier to program, and the data are precise. The old way was less precise, but the operator was unlikely to insert a data point that was an order of magnitude in error, or with two digits reversed. Which is better?

There are cases where precision *is* required in analogue systems, and then typical 'digital errors' do occur even there. A case in point is that of the multiple pointer analogue altimeter (Figure 3.2(a)), used in post-World War II aircraft to display altitudes up to several tens of thousands of feet, yet see a

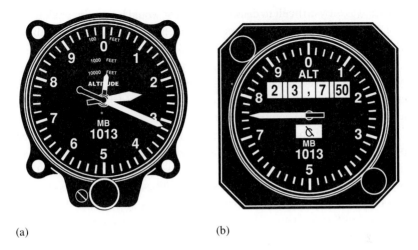

(a)   (b)

Figure 3.2   (a) Analogue altimeter with three ranges. The large pointer indicates hundreds of feet, the middle pointer thousands and the small one tens of thousands. The three pointers are easily confused.
(b) A better design: a combined digital and analogue altimeter. The drum gives digital accuracy over a wide range while the pointer shows how the altitude is changing.

change of several feet. The instrument's small pointer indicated 10,000 ft per division, the middle one 1000 ft per division and the longest pointer 100 ft per division. Many aeroplane crashes were attributed to misreading these altimeters under stress, mistaking the 100 ft pointer for the 10,000 ft one, etc. This type of instrument was finally replaced by the 'drum and pointer' type altimeter (Figure 3.2(b)) with a single pointer and a Veeder counter digital readout. This altimeter combines the best of both worlds; the digital readout provides precision and wide range, while the pointer provides a natural sense of 'how things are changing'. The frequency of occurrence of altimeter misreading decreased sharply[11].

It is well known that it is very difficult to identify a discrepancy in a long list of numbers. Both manual and automatic techniques have been developed to overcome this problem. For example, a 'checksum' number computed once when the list is generated, and another time when the list is inserted into the process control computer. If the checksums do not match, at least one number is wrong. This will not help if the original list is wrong too, as occurred in the 1979 crash of an Air New Zealand DC–10 on Mount Erebus[12]. There, the captain used the list of waypoint co-ordinates to plot his course on a map to prepare for the flight. He was not informed that the list he received just before the flight for insertion into his navigation computer was slightly different. The difference was very difficult to detect on a list, but would have been obvious on a map: the track was now leading directly to a mountain, instead of going above sea-level ice (see Chapter 1, Section 7, page 33).

Returning to process control, a computerized system makes it rather easy to provide operators with monitoring information; it is all in the system. You do not need a costly gauge or plotter to present the data to the operators; you just display it on the computer screen.

The problem becomes one of information congestion: there is no place to put all that data on the screen. There are many methods of dealing with that, besides the obvious (but costly) use of a computer to drive 'old-style' displays, or using multiple screens. Some of these possibilities are a menu system that allows only data requested by the operator to show, a system that shows data only when it differs from normal conditions, data that show only when an alarm condition exists, etc.

All these devices suffer from several problems that may become serious in an emergency:
- the impact of information that is not on the screen is not appreciated;
- in an emergency situation, the operators may become so occupied with the problem at hand that they will not scan through the menus for other problems that may be developing;
- potential confusion between two different pieces of information which show at different times at the same place;
- messages may flash past too quickly, and their impact may not be appreciated;
- an alarm is an alarm only if it was programmed to be so. The undesigned-for conditions may lead to disasters (see also Chapter 1, Section 5, page 26).

Two examples of such phenomena (although not in situations directly involving computers) are the 1972 fatal crash of an Eastern Airlines L–1011, and the 1967 fatal crash of an X–15 research aeroplane. In the Eastern case, the crew was fixing a minor problem with a landing gear position indicator (the bulbs burned out), with the plane on automatic pilot. The autopilot apparently disengaged, but the crew was so occupied with the task at hand that they disregarded both their instruments and an aural warning before the crash[13]. In the X–15 case, the sequence of events leading to the crash started with a minor problem. It occupied the pilot so much that he apparently misinterpreted a dual-mode display as showing one flight parameter while it was actually showing the other, with disastrous results[14].

Up till now I have described data entry and data display. Plant control also involves actuation: telling the system what to do. The natural tendency of designers of computerized systems is to use traditional computer controls: a

'telling the system what to do'

keyboard and a pointing device (mouse, tracker ball, or a light-pen); cheap, standard, and all-powerful when combined with the right software. What we do lose is the 'human touch' as seen in the frequent use of 'memorable' shape controls in critical facilities — 'beer-dispenser' control levers in nuclear plant control rooms, wheel-shaped landing gear levers in aircraft cockpits and so on. These provide not only memory enhancements, but a different level of physical contact between operator and plant.

One important subject to be considered is the basic human tendency to trust a seemingly intelligent computer. The more automatic and reliable the process, the more the operator is reduced to passive monitoring, and is inclined to subconsciously assume that the computer is 'never wrong'. If something does go wrong, the operator's responses may be different from the case where there is a frequent need to intervene actively (see Chapter 1, item 8.1, page 33).

To quote Reference 13, 'Another problem concerns the new automatic systems which are coming into service with newer aircraft and being added to older aircraft. Flight crews become more reliant upon the functioning of sophisticated avionics systems, and their associated automation, to fly the airplane. This is increasingly so as the reliability of such equipment improves. Basic control of the aircraft and supervision of the flight's progress by instrument indications diminish as other more pressing tasks in the cockpit attract attention because of the over-reliance on such automatic equipment ... Pilots' testimony indicated that dependence on the reliability and capability of the autopilot is actually greater than anticipated in its early design and its certification'.

11.   MALICIOUS PROGRAMS

Large quantities translate into low prices and high performance. Thus, the best computer equipment value is probably obtained by using popular systems such as advanced IBM compatible PCs, or RISC (reduced instruction set computer) workstations. Also, the best value for the software that underlies application programs is one of the commercial operating systems (OS), such as MS-DOS or Unix. Even when the process control computer is a programmable logic controller (PLC), a popular computer is mostly used to generate its programs, utilizing the sophisticated development support facilities (compilers, debuggers, etc) available for the popular computers. As PCs and workstations proliferate, we may find them controlling plants too.

Popular computers and operating systems have lately attracted the attention of malicious programmers. They have created a host of malignant programs that attach themselves to normal programs and OS facilities, to create mayhem at a later date. These programs include viruses, Trojan horses, worms and other vicious species[15]. Some of these are designed to start creating damage after they have infected enough programs, some stay dormant until 'something' occurs — for example, Friday the thirteenth or the fiftieth anniversary of the death of Hitler. Viruses are usually transmitted through computer networks and illegitimate copies of software diskettes. There have been cases of contaminated brand new, legitimate software, perhaps created by a disgruntled programmer at the source.

Numerous 'anti-virus' programs are available, but they can only hunt down *known* virus classes, or those that infected the computer following installation of the anti-virus program. Trojan horses, for instance, are installed as a part of a legitimate program that serves a legitimate function. They strike when triggered — by a set date, by an I/O operations count, or perhaps by lack of a predefined input once a month, indicating that the perpetrator has been fired. Since they come as part of an original program, they cannot be detected by an anti-virus program. Only one unconfirmed report of a malignant software attack against a safety-related computer installation has appeared so far (see Chapter 1, item 8.4, page 35). Nevertheless, we cannot be sure that a malignant program is not lurking underneath our plant control program, waiting for its trigger.

As an aside, so far I have had four encounters with viruses. Two of them were introduced into my system by maintenance people who came to fix minor hardware problems. Caveat computor!

12.   CLASSICS

Some errors have become 'classics'; everybody in the business knows about them, and facilities are designed to prevent them. Yet they do appear again and again, partly because people forget, partly because these facilities are associated with performance penalties which may be deemed unacceptable. Here are some examples:

12.1   INITIALIZATION ERRORS

One of the more horrible computer crashes I have experienced involved a large artificial intelligence program that ran reliably for quite a time. It ran several times during a long weekend before it finally 'crashed', bringing down the whole computer system with it.

It turned out that the program was using rather complicated data structures to describe the external world. Each time the program encountered a situation, it had to determine whether it was a new one, or one that it had seen before. This was done by checking whether an appropriate data structure already existed, and this — in turn — was done by checking whether a header contained one of ten distinct patterns. If it did not, then it was a new situation and a data structure had to be created. If it did, then the existing data structure was to be used.

There was an error in the program; it did not initialize its memory space properly, and so the header patterns it encountered in 'new situations' were random. The chance of encountering one of ten given patterns in a random 64-bit header is about 5×10^{-20}; in other words, a very slim chance of anything going wrong. So what happened?

The answer lies in the long weekend. The computer being used was an IBM mainframe, in which each running program is allocated an arbitrary memory slice by the multitasking operating system. Each program's uninitialized memory locations contain seemingly random bit patterns, which are actually parts of other programs previously run in the same slice. During the long weekend the queue of 'batch' jobs ran out, and nobody was using it for interactive work. So, on its final run, our program received — for the first time in its existence — exactly the same physical memory slice it received on its previous run.

Now, of course, the patterns were not random any more, and the inevitable crash occurred.

12.2 LANGUAGE

Computer language designers strive to give the programmer the best tools they can, to enhance productivity and make the code produced more efficient, less error-prone, and more 'reusable'. Designing each language feature involves some hard choices between these goals. Reference 16 reviews several languages from a safety point of view.

If a program generates a variable, it stands to reason that it is going to be used at some point. Similarly, if a label is defined somewhere in the program, it was probably meant to be used as an address to go to from another place in the program. Failure to do either is indicative of hidden problems, and indeed modern computer language compilers warn the programmer of such occurrences. But then, not all programs are written using modern languages, and checks can sometimes be bypassed.

One example is of an early all-digital missile system. A safety review committee advised, quite late in development, to add a safety enhancement involving an extra controller program check.

The control program loop started, appropriately enough, with the label 'begin'. An obvious choice for the label of the new entry point required by the enhancement was 'begin1'. That choice was out, however, since it exceeded the compiler's maximum label string length of five characters.

Actually, the language designers intended to provide for better program documentation by allowing *any* length label strings (as in begin_safety_check_1). The compiler designers, however, implemented this feature by *ignoring* all characters following the first five*. Everybody was aware of the trap set by that language feature, and long names were avoided like the plague. The programmer's choice was therefore a foreshortened 'bgin1'. A typographical error 'goto begin1' was not noticed, resulting in the '1' being dropped from the goto address. The program flow at that point went to 'begin' rather than to 'bgin1'. That introduced an extra time delay into the control loop, which caused the missile to go out of control and crash.

---

* Another language of that era catered for this situation by setting a limit of eight characters, and allowing unlimited string length by ignoring all but the first five and the last three characters. It is debatable whether that eased or worsened the problem.

13.   SOME ADVICE

Probably the best advice is to 'think ahead', be it by means of Hazop, Chazop, FMECA or any other methodology advocated in the previous chapters. As for the computer software part of the system under consideration, a general point of advice is to follow 'good

engineering practice'. Some of these practices are top-down specifications, rigid configuration control and multilevel walkthrough reviews[2].

The following is some specific advice to system designers and managers in charge of design or maintenance of safety-sensitive installations.

13.1   HARDWARE GATEKEEPERS

Most of the problems described so far have had to do with software, the component of any computer system that gives it its real power. Obviously, any protection device that relies on software running together with the process control program must suffer, in principle, from the same problems. The obvious solution is to include in the system separate hardware for detection and prevention of hazardous situations (see Chapter 1, item 3.1, page 11). Note that this separate hardware may include computers too. Here are some examples:

13.1.1   WATCHDOGS

Most of the software error situations described in the previous sections — Win-Fax (Section 4, page 84), the M-plot (Section 9, page 94), etc — involve computers 'freezing up' while executing a task. One frequent solution is a 'watchdog', made up of a software and a hardware component. Process control programs always operate in repetitive cycles, so the software part of the watchdog is made up of a few statements, executed once in each cycle, that issues a signal to an external device. That device is the hardware part of the watchdog, and it is set up to expect such a signal every so often. If a signal is missed (or signals are received too frequently), the device initiates an *independent* safety action.

13.1.2   MULTIPLE COMPUTERS

Two (or more) computers may be set up to analyse the process data in parallel, in one of several schemes. The simplest involves two identical computers using identical software, and a discrepancy detector that shuts down the process in a safe manner. The logic here is that since it cannot be determined automatically which computer is right, we had better shut down. Another scheme is 'majority voting', in which three or more computers work in parallel, and a voter decides which result to use and which computer to shut down.

Both schemes suffer from the fact that software errors common to all the computers involved are not detected. One solution is to have two (or more) computers running different software. For example, one computer runs the regular process control algorithm, while the other runs a much simplified — and presumably, less error-prone — algorithm. The output of the second computer is used for bound checking, rather then exact comparison. Another example is to have two or more equal-quality (but different!) sets of software written by completely different teams, running in parallel. Such schemes (which are known as N-version programming[17]) are usually expensive to implement, but may be essential for safety-critical processes that cannot be interrupted, such as flight control of marginally-stable aircraft (see Chapter 1, item 3.1, page 10). One disturbing phenomenon is that errors common to all N versions still appear with higher frequency then warranted by assumptions of independence[18,19].

All schemes suffer from an inherent problem concerning the reliability of the discrepancy detector/voter: it is an extra piece of equipment and software that is subject to failure by itself, and is common to all the computers involved. But, in that sense, it is not different from any other piece of process control equipment ... .

13.2   REVIEW AND TEST

There can never be too much testing for a computerized control system. As shown earlier, there can also never be enough testing — it just takes too much time. So, how do you test? There is a large body of advice on test procedures, the essence of which is summed up nicely in the title of the book, *The Art of Software Testing*[20]. In other words, it is an art, not a science. And good advice it does give — from 'walkthrough' reviews to module testing to system testing. I mention only two items here:

13.2.1   TEST FACILITY

Use a 'hybrid' simulator as much as possible, 'hybrid' in the sense that it contains both the actual process computer and another computer/hardware simulating the external world. The main concern is to run the process computer in a 'closed loop', interacting with an independent external model of the world. Problems such as instability due to slight time delays introduced through errors (see Section 12.2, page 102) stand a better chance of being detected this way.

Also, try to use real hardware interface modules between the two. For example, use the real analogue to digital converters (ADCs), fed by simulation digital to analogue converters (DACs), rather then direct digital connections: running ADCs requires different software drivers, and the fine characteristics of data coming in are different from directly-transmitted digital data.

13.2.2   TEST SETS

A 'test set' is the ensemble of conditions and inputs that exercise a system during tests. As mentioned in Section 6 (see page 88), it is impossible to go through a set that covers *all* possible paths through any practical software. Instead, we try to make the test set as representative as possible. One result is that most testing involves software that is executed frequently. It has been observed, however, that a disproportionate amount of failure occurs due to software that is rarely executed[21]. This is even more true when several rare events happen on top of each other. The trouble is, the possible number of rare events — and their combinations — is very large, so how do we assemble a good test set?

The practice that evolved in the author's group was to assemble a two-part test set. One part was defined by specifying each of the system's normal operating parameter limits, and selecting values within these limits using probability functions. Note that some parameter combinations would place the system as a whole outside its design limits, even though each individual parameter is within its limits. Thus, the test set included some rare and unusual cases.

A group (nicknamed 'Council of the Ayatollahs') was convened to define the second part of the test set. The Council was composed of senior system engineers, operators, software specialists and a human factors expert. Each was asked to submit his own set of failure-prone conditions. The Council's set was a mixture of 'classics', estimates of where conditions were likely to deviate from the nominal, rare conditions inadequately covered otherwise and just plain gut-feelings*. All test cases were run and compared with their design behaviour, allowing for a reasonable tolerance due to simulation imperfections.

An important note: the test set should not be available to the programming/debugging team prior to start of the formal test. Otherwise, it is a fixed game!

13.3   REVIEWS

Quite often an independent review is very effective. The question is, 'what do we review?'

A story: a chief programmer for a missile project was modifying the control program code when he was called to a meeting that lasted several hours. After the meeting he went home. Checking the code the next day everything seemed all right.

In reality, the change in the code *was* all right, but a comment describing a modification of the use of one intermediate variable was not updated.

Comments are plain English text inserted into a program code to explain what the program — or a particular step in the program — does. Thorough commenting is considered good programming practice, providing 'in-place' documentation for program maintenance. A comment is not executed, of course, so the omission did not have any effect on the way the program runs.

Several weeks later another modification was made. Going by the comments, the programmer used that memory address as if it still contained the original variable. This modification passed review and unit test.

The error was discovered when the chief programmer recalled the incident some time later, while going through the code looking for something else. Analysis showed that it would have caused the missile to become unstable when pointing to a certain sector while flying in a certain speed regime. That particu-

---

*   Reference 19 contains a list of fault conditions obtained from 27 different programs written to the same specification. The abundance of common conditions indicates that experience and 'gut-feelings' are valid factors here.

lar combination of conditions would not have been exercised during planned testing, but could have caused a severe hazard in operational use.

The moral of the story is: not all is what it seems. Reviewers quite often go by a description of the code, rather than by the code itself. This description is called 'documentation', and is composed of multiple levels — requirements, specifications, algorithms, various levels of design documents, flow charts, program source and, finally, the code itself. It is an error to assume that all documentation hierarchy is consistent, both within itself, and with the eventual code. A good (and necessarily lengthy) review has to check everything[2].

13.4   POST-MORTEM

If (or rather, when) something does occur — be it an accident or a 'near-miss' — the immediate thrust is to solve the problem at hand. Quite often the cure is 'obvious', and the problem is quickly eliminated.

Experience shows that it pays to dig deeper: the 'obvious' cure is often wrong. More thorough analysis often reveals that the source of the problem is somewhere else. And, once a fault has been found, we should always try to understand the mechanisms by which it was created. Understanding these, one can then look for other places where similar mechanisms could have led to creation of more faults.

Thus, the Therac–25 accidents described in Chapter 1, item 3.2.1 (page 13) were caused by a software error ('bug') triggered by a 'cursor up', followed by rapid data entry on the machine's operator's console. Examination of Reference 22 shows that:

• two similar 'cursor up' problems were found in 'service mode' — and considered corrected — in 1985;

• an incident in July 1985 in Hamilton, Ontario, Canada, was attributed to a design weakness, which made the machine overly sensitive to transient failures

in microswitch signals. The presence of such failure was never actually verified;
- an incident in Tyler, Texas, USA, in March 1986 was attributed to electric shock;
- the 'cursor up' bug was blamed only following another incident in Tyler in April 1986;
- the same bug appeared in the earlier Therac–20 but, due to hardware interlocks, it manifested itself only in blown fuses and tripped circuit breakers. These were evidently not considered serious enough at the time to merit investigation;
- an incident in Yakima Valley, Washington, USA, in January 1987 revealed one more software bug, one that appeared when the operator hit the 'set' button at the precise moment that a certain loop had been executed 256 times.

Note the reference to a transient microswitch failure. Aviation accident investigators have to avoid the temptation to blame 'pilot error'; it is the easy solution and therefore often wrong. Also, if the pilot erred, was there a 'reason why'? Similarly, investigators of computer-related problems have to avoid blaming 'transient hardware problems'; too many software bugs can be erroneously attributed to such transients.

13.5 DATA FOR A RAINY DAY

The first Therac–25 fatal accidents were attributed to transient problems with the machine's turntable microswitches[22]. True, the logic design of the switch set-up was flawed, so if a transient did occur it could trigger a mishap, but did it really occur?

The basic problem here is lack of information pointing to the source of the failure. Unlike most physical processes, software faults do not leave any telltale signs to indicate to the post-mishap investigator how the failure occurred. Once a finger is pointed at a particular small area, the fault is usually quickly located. In many situations, however, that finger has disappeared a long time before the investigators come in, and a bit in an 'unlimited propagation space' (see Section 7, page 90) is far worse then the proverbial needle in a haystack.

Aircraft accident investigation used to suffer from a similar basic problem — impact or post-impact fire, destroying all information pointing to the source of a crash. One of the major steps towards improving airline flight safety was the mandatory introduction of fire- and crash-resistant cockpit voice recorders (CVRs) and flight data recorders (FDRs) into airliners in the early sixties. The recorders' presence did not reduce the probability of that aircraft crashing, but by improving the probability of finding and correcting the true cause of the crash, it helped to prevent accidents in generations to come. Indeed, the odds of being killed in a commercial flight halved in the years following that act[23].

Similar thinking should go into the design of computerized plant control systems. It is fairly straightforward to keep on magnetic media a certain backlog of important software events: sensor inputs, program branches, watchdog operations, outputs and so on. If nothing happens, the media are erased and reused every so often. If something does happen, the data could make quite a difference ... (see Chapter 1, item 5.4, page 28).

14. BRAVE NEW WORLD (1)

There is a growing body of research concerning 'formal methods' and a definitive survey has been published[24]. These methods seek to improve the quality of software by expressing its specifications in a formal notation, and using them in one or more of the following:

- checking the specifications for consistency and completeness;
- generating the machine code directly from the specifications, either automatically or semi-automatically;
- validating, or proving the correctness of the code.

Unfortunately[25], formal methods have been promoted in the past as a panacea for all the ills of software, thus violating one of the basic rules of engineering ('There is no panacea'). Formal methods do hold a promise for improving software quality, but unfortunately again, that promise will apparently not be fulfilled for some time[24].

My main reason for expressing doubt in the bright future of formal methods is that, for them to work in a system environment, both the software specifications and the outside world have to be rigorously expressed in mathematically-tractable terms. The 'outside world' here includes everything that is relevant except the specified software: devices and processes, time and space, all other software, human operators, etc. The ultimate specifier — the generator of the basic requirement — is a human being, and the specifications are merely means of communicating that person's desires to the agents that generate and check the final code. The real question is then whether mathematical notation is the most robust, error-free means of communicating human desire, and I am not sure at all that it is.

15. BRAVE NEW WORLD (2)

The world of computers is a fast-moving one, while safety people tend to be justifiably conservative. A likely item for the agenda of computer safety is expert systems, a branch of artificial intelligence (AI).

AI is a general field of research on intelligent behaviour by computers[26]. The idea behind expert systems is to try to capture experts' knowledge in a computer program and try either to assist or replace people performing the experts' work. Considerable success has been achieved by such systems — for example, in managing product configurations, analysing chemical structures, troubleshooting equipment and playing chess. Success has been such that people in the field have begun to worry about the legal liability they may incur if their products fail[27,28].

Imitating an expert's complex thought processes is no easy task. Consider, for example, how you figure out to 'get from here to there'; do you start with 'from here' and go forward, start with 'to there' and go backwards, or maybe start from both ends?

More and more software tools for building expert systems software ('AI shells') are arriving on the market, and more systems are being built using them. A typical shell[29] gives the programmer a framework for building a 'knowledge base' composed of application-specific definitions and rules, and an 'inference engine', a program that applies the rules to data to arrive at conclusions about what to do.

That sounds simple, but think about it: what really happens when a plant control room supervisor asks an expert operator, 'what is the temperature of that vat?'. If they are talking about a slow process, and a temperature reading has been taken recently, the reply will probably be the value of the last reading. If the last reading is 'stale', the operator will go out and take a new reading, unless taking the reading takes a long time, and the operator knows that the supervisor needs the answer right away. In this case extrapolating the sequence of readings gives an answer, unless the operator knows from experience that the process going on in that vat is given to lots of variations. Here, a fresh reading will be taken anyhow.

A good shell handles all of this — at a price. Part of the price is, often, a degradation in the 'ability to test' department. More important, documenting and understanding what is *really* going on becomes rather difficult. Remaining with the same example, the action of the operator deciding to go out and take an actual reading may or may not trigger an action of opening the control room door. If the door is stuck, an action of going for an oil can may be called for. Once out in the rain, the operator may decide to note some other instrument readings to avoid having to come out again soon. And if one of the readings seems abnormal there may be a temptation to initiate something else on the side.

I vividly recall trying to understand the behaviour of one such program, and finding out (the hard way) that the parameter that determined most of what happened was the validity period for a certain measurement. That particular parameter did not even appear in the program's flow documentation.

One of the subfields of AI is natural language understanding — so the 'When I nod my head, hit it' vignette (Chapter 1, Figure 1.5, page 18) may not be so funny after all. Watch out!

16.   CONCLUSIONS

This chapter can be nicely summed up in a quotation from an anonymous source:

'If the auto industry were like the computer industry, a car would now cost $50, would travel 500 miles per gallon, and at a random time would explode, killing all passengers.'

Industrial efficiency benefits from the first two elements of the quotation. It is safety's mission to prevent the third. This chapter points out that the mission is not easy, and in practical terms may be impossible. What can be done is:

- think ahead;
- be careful; and
- never trust software alone.

Also, as technology moves ahead, *never take anything for granted*. For instance, if the machine in charge of your production process is a mere programmable controller, you are immune to compatibility problems. Right? A controller is not a PC or a workstation, does not have a disk drive, and there is no operating system, just a burned-in program, no viruses, thank you. Right?

But when the time comes to upgrade the facility, the controller program has to be changed. Now, how is the new program generated? Isn't that on a PC? And wasn't that PC running DOS 3.1 when the original version was written, and is running DOS 6.22 now? And didn't they throw out all the ATs and replace them with Pentium machines in mid-1994? Aha! What do the equations for the pressure setpoint values look like? How accurate do the division operations have to be? Did Bob take up Intel's offer to replace Pentium chips with ones without the FDIV bug, or was he just too busy at the time?

I rest my case.

REFERENCES IN CHAPTER 3

1.   Leveson, N.G., 1986, *ACM Computing Surveys*, 18 (2): 125.
2.   Parnas, D. *et al*, 1990, *Communications of the ACM*, 33 (6): 636.

3. Neumann, P.G. (Moderator), Risks to the public in computers and related systems, appears periodically in *ACM SIGSOFT Software Engineering Notes* (for an example, see the January 1992 issue).

4. Brooks, F.P., 1975, *The Mythical Man-Month — Essays on Software Engineering* (Edison-Wesley, Reading, MA, USA).

5. December 1994, items on the Internet NEWS group COMP.SYS.INTEL, especially items by Nicely, T., Coe, T. and Moler, C..

6. Colonel Garrett's testimony, in 'Performance of the Patriot Missile in the Gulf war', Hearing before the Legislation and National Security Subcommittee of the Committee on Government Operations, House of Representatives, Washington, DC, USA, 7 April 1992.

7. Postol, T.A., 1991, *International Security*, 16 (3): Winter 1991/1992.

8. Boehm, B.W., January 1970, *Some Information Processing Implications of Air Force Space Missions, RAND Memorandum RM–6213–PR*.

9. Smith, R., 1986, *PC Tech Journal*, 4 (4): 56.

10. Battin, R., October 1994, On algebraic compilers and planetary fly-by orbits, *45th Congress of the International Astronautical Federation, Jerusalem, Israel.*

11. Pallett, E.H.J., 1972, *Aircraft Instruments* (Pitman, London).

12. Stewart, S., 1986, *Air Disasters* (Ian Allen, London), 172.

13. National Transportation Safety Board, June 1973, *Report NTSB–AAR–73–14: Aircraft Accident Report — Eastern Air Lines Inc., L–1011 N310EA, Miami, Florida, December 29, 1972* (Washington, DC, USA).

14. NASA board of review into the destruction of the No. 3 North American Rockwell X–15, reported in *Aviation Week & Space Technology*, 12 August 1968 and subsequent issues.

15. Burger, R., 1987, *Computer Viruses and Data Protection* (Abacus, Grand Rapids, MI, USA).

16. Cullyer, W.J., Goodenough, S.J. and Wickmann, B.A., 1991, *Software Engineering Journal*, 62 (2): 51.

17. Chen, L. and Avizienis, A., June 1978, N–Version programming: a fault-tolerant approach to reliability of software operation, in *Dig. FTCS–8: Eighth Annual International Symposium on Fault-Tolerant Computing, Toulouse, France.*

18. Knight, J.C. and Leveson, N.G., 1986, *IEEE Transactions on Software Engineering*, 12 (1): 96.

19. Brilliant, S.S., Knight. J.C. and Leveson N.G., 1990, *IEEE Transactions on Software Engineering*, 16 (2): 238.

20. Myers, G., 1979, *The Art of Software Testing* (Wiley, New York).

21. Hecht, H., 1993, Rare conditions — an important cause of failure, in *COMPASS 93 — Eighth Annual Conference on Computer Assurance, Gaithersburg, MD, USA.*

22. Leveson, N.G. and Turner, C.S., 1993, *IEEE Computer*, 26 (7): 18.

23. Barnett, A., Abraham, M. and Schimmel, V., 1979, *Management Science*, 25 (11): 1045.

24. Bowen, J. and Stravridou, V., 1993, *Software Engineering Journal*, 8 (4): 189.

25. Hall, A., 1990, *IEEE Software*, 7 (5): 11.

26. Feigenbaum, E. and Feldman, J., 1963, *Computers and Thought* (McGraw-Hill, New York).

27. Gemignani, M., 1990, Liability for malfunction of an expert system, Keynote address in *IEEE Conference on Managing Expert Systems Programs and Projects, Bethesda, MD, USA.*

28. Sprague, R. and Berkowitz, L., 1990, Potential theories of legal liability for defective expert system software, *IEEE Conference on Managing Expert Systems Programs and Projects, Bethesda, MD, USA.*

29. Gensym Corporation, 1990, *G2 Reference Manual for Version 2.0 of the G2 Real-Time Expert System* (Gensym Corporation, Cambridge, MA, USA).

AFTERTHOUGHTS

The following quotations are taken from a publication (Dutton, W.H. *et al*, *Computer Control and Human Limits: Learning from IT and Telecommunications Disasters — A Forum Discussion*, Programme on Information & Communication Technologies, Brunel University, Uxbridge, UK) that appeared while this book was in production.

'A striking feature of most major failures we discussed was that most could probably have been avoided if existing knowledge about effective systems design, development and information had been applied.'

W.H. Dutton

'As soon as a manager in the smallest particular is allowed to believe that such intangibility [of software] gives an excuse for not knowing and understanding, there is a lift off from reality. And what starts out as a loss of touch by an inch quickly becomes a mile ...'

C.A.R. Hoare (see Chapter 1, item 4.1, page 17)

'... in the stock market ... brokers with acquired expert and intuitive skills are being replaced by those whose skills lie in playing with electronic models.'

G.I. Rochlin (see Chapter 1, item 5.5, page 28)

'... the actual history of ICT [information and communication technology] disasters compared favourably with the history of general engineering developments.'

N. Boothman

The next four quotations refer to the failure of the London Ambulance Service Computer-Aided Despatch System in 1992:

*'There was no evidence of questions being
asked about the winning bid, such as why it
was so much lower than others.'*

*'... in mission-critical software, ... negative
assurance [such as, "there is no evidence to suggest
that the full system software, when commissioned,
will not prove reliable"] ... is not enough.'*

(Compare the report on the sinking of the ferry *Herald of Free Enterprise* in 1987; the captain assumed the bow doors had been closed unless someone told him they were not.)

*'The final crash ... was caused by a small
piece of code which caused the system to eat
up all available memory.'*

*'Many managers and staff saw deadlines set
by the top level of management as being rigid,
inflexible and, more importantly, not to be
challenged at the risk of losing one's job or
being moved sideways.'*

(Compare the reports on the loss of the space shuttle *Challenger* in 1986.)

The next quotation refers to the shooting down of an Iranian passenger aircraft by the US Navy in 1987:

*[A relatively junior officer] 'appears to have
suffered from "scenario fulfilment", in which
data flow is distorted in an unconscious attempt to
make available evidence fit a preconceived scenario.'*

*'A recent UK Ministry of Defence Study could
not find any feasibility study which had come up
with the politically unacceptable conclusion that
the project would* not *be feasible.'*

J. Dobson

'... there was widespread agreement that the ability to manage evolving requirements efficiently should be accepted as the norm ...'

'While contracting out can be effective, it should never go so far as destroying any residual in-house expertise ...'

'... there is some evidence of a tendency to take the action recommended by the computer, despite serious questions in the user's mind.'

G.I. Rochlin (compare Chapter 1, item 8.1, page 33 and Section 9, page 36)

'... the person in charge of the safety-control computers at a nuclear plant in Lithuania was recently found to have placed a virus in the system so that he could help in the investigation which found it. He wanted to demonstrate that he was an important person.'

(Compare Chapter 1, item 8.4, page 35.)

FURTHER READING

Safeware: System Safety and Computers by N.G. Leveson (Addison-Wesley, Reading, MA, USA, 1995, 680 pages) was published while this book was in production. I recommend it to readers who would like to follow up in greater detail many of the subjects discussed in this book.

Trevor Kletz

INDEX